1-23-10

And Should We Die...

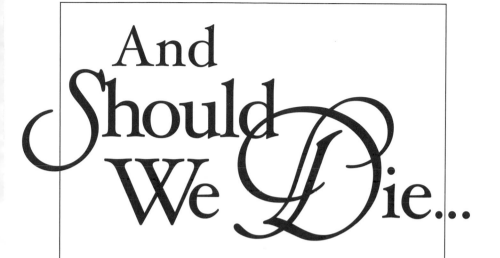

And Should We Die...

A YOUNG MAN'S EXPERIENCE
WITH THE MIRACULOUS

By the **The New York Times** Best-selling Author
Ron McMillan
& Randy McMillan

American Family Publications
Idaho Falls, Idaho

Table of Contents

We dedicate this book to:

To our parents, Howard and Beverly McMillan, who possess the patience of Job and have suffered through nearly as many trials. They both are angels of the Lord and continue even now in his service.

and

To my wife, Bonnie Marie McMillan, whose life of love and sacrifice exemplifies the powerful principles Randy learned and taught.

Acknowledgements

This book is a gift of love and we acknowledge those who have given so much.

To **Stephen R. Covey, Alan Wilkins, and Gene Dalton**, a special thanks for their influence and direction, without which this book would never have been completed.

For their gifts of intelligence, thoughtfulness, and inspiration in the editing effort, we thank Janiel Miller, Tamara Murray, Elaine Weinkauf, and Melba Christison.

For contributing memories, testimony, and themselves, a heartfelt thank you to Beverly McMillan, Blake McMillan, Dan and Alicia McMillan, Diane Henderson, Earl and Melba Christison, and a host of family, friends, and loved ones.

For their miraculous ability to translate volumes of nearly indecipherable handwriting into printed words, many thanks to Laura Breaux, Mindy Childs, and Charla Allen.

For their gifts of creativity with the book cover and design, thanks to Rob Davis and Amber Linebaugh.

For entrusting so much that is personal and sacred, we acknowledge Lance Richardson. Thank you.

For being patient with Ron's absences and supportive of his writing, eternal gratitude to my children: Amber, Megan, Chase, Hayley, Bryn, Amberly, Laura, Rebecca, Rachael, and Benjamin.

And Should We Die . . .

Prologue

The voice on the phone was a low, raspy whisper, "Hey Ron . . . it's me . . . Lance."

"Lance?" I repeated.

"Yeah."

"Lance Richardson?"

"Yeah."

"Really! I can't believe it! Is this really you? You're talking!" I shouted. "The doctors said you wouldn't be able to speak for three or four months. What's it been, one week?"

"Yeah . . . something . . . like . . . that." He sounded so weak. I realized suddenly that he must be talking through his tracheotomy tube.

"Well, after you've regained your strength . . ."

"Ron," Lance interrupted. "I've been there."

"What?"

"I . . . have . . . been . . . there."

"Been where?"

"I saw . . . Randy. Talked . . . to him."

"Uh, Lance," I reminded him, "Randy died over 20 years ago." *Maybe it was his medication talking*, I thought.

"I . . . saw . . . him ," Lance was tiring; he was barely audible. "I . . . talked . . . with him . . . He gave . . . me . . . a message . . . to give you . . . Its . . . im . . . portant . . . that . . . we . . . get . . . to . . . gether."

I was stunned. "Okay, okay, we'll drive up to Idaho right away."

"Thanks . . . Ron. Give love . . . to Bonnie. . . . See you . . . soon."

I hung up the phone and sat down hard in the chair. The memory of a day in my office nearly 23 years ago overwhelmed me and I could think of nothing else.

Chapter 1

A Little Grayer

"And so you see, my young friends . . ." I then paused for dramatic effect and turned away from the class. I slid the moveable half of the chalkboard to the right and revealed the carefully printed message. Stepping to the side, I read it aloud: "Death is not the end, but merely a change of scenery."

I turned back—too late to duck. Two large spitballs coming from opposite sides of the room were already on their downward trajectory. One hit my forehead. The other landed in my ear and stuck.

At first the class was shocked—all wide eyes and open mouths. Then someone started snickering, and the silent room exploded with laughter. Though I shook my head and tried to look indignant, I could only resist for a moment. I turned so everyone had a better view of the white plug in my ear. The students went crazy, some hooting, some slapping their desks. We laughed for a full minute.

The bell rang. And as they stood up to leave, I yelled, "Wait, wait!" I then assumed mock seriousness.

"My dear brothers and sisters, don't forget to re-read First Nephi, chapter fifteen and always remember . . . the Gospel's true."

As the class clamored out, Cynthia predictably approached and said "Brother McMillan, that was a very special lesson."

"Thank you, Cynthia." She smiled and a moment later my room was empty and quiet.

I was sure that Nathan and Todd were the spitball assassins; I hoped they were getting something out of the class. I found them both difficult to read. I was just beginning my second year of teaching seminary. Students at the high school were released one class period a day for religious instruction. I loved teaching both the subject and the students, and I hoped I was accomplishing some good.

The next period was my free period. I had a lot of preparation to do for the next day's lessons and was anxious to get started. I picked up my materials and walked into my adjoining office.

Randy was sitting in my chair, his feet propped up on my desk. He was wearing his usual attire—dirty Converse tennis shoes, well-worn Levis, a plaid shirt, and that silly navy-blue stocking cap pulled down to the top of his ears.

He smiled up at me and said, "Hey Bro."

The autumn sun illuminated the yellow birch leaves outside the window, and as they fluttered in the breeze, my little room was filled with dancing golden light.

I emptied the contents of my arms onto the file cabinet and leaned against my desk, facing Randy. He looked tired.

"This is a surprise," I said. "Have you been waiting long?"

"No. I was on my way down to the library and thought I'd drop by. Do you have a few minutes?"

A Little Grayer

"Sure. You're looking good."

Giving me a half-smile he replied, "I'm not feeling so good." He looked out the window at the leaves. "I think it's about over."

I wasn't sure what he meant.

"Did you hear about my speech in Bountiful?" he asked. "There were over a thousand people there, and afterward, people formed a long line to thank me. Several were crying and couldn't talk. I reached to shake hands with one man and he just grabbed me, gave me a big hug, and said 'You'll never know how much you helped me tonight. Thank you.'"

Tears welled up in Randy's eyes. He blinked and quickly looked away. "I think I'm helping a lot of people. I really feel like I've been doing good. I think its about over, and I don't want it to end."

I walked behind him. I started massaging his shoulders and he leaned his head back against me.

"Actually, I do want it to end. I'm so tired. There's thirty seconds left in the last round and I just want it to be over."

His neck muscles were taut and hard. I rubbed them with my knuckles in small circles. He bowed his head and mumbled, "Feels good." I ran my fingers along the hairline between his ears. His hair was wispy and thin like an old man's. The skin against his skull was almost transparent, and it seemed very fragile—like it might tear if I rubbed too hard.

"Randy, I know the last little while has been really hard for you. You're feeling down and that's natural. But it's going to get better. It always does."

Randy slowly turned in the chair until he was facing me.

"Ron, I'm going to die, and I think it will be soon. And I'm glad. Sometimes it feels like there's acid inside, eating me away—it burns, it hurts something awful. I'm going to be glad to step outside this body and let it go. But I feel sad too. I've helped a lot of people, I know I've made a real difference. But there are a lot of people out there that I know I can help. I want to reach them. I want to help them. To die now would be to abandon them. It's like I'm serving people in a soup line who need the food, and I'm happy to give it and they thank me. But I've been going several days without sleep and I need rest. Yet to stop means some will starve."

"You can't feed the whole world! It's not all up to you," I said forcefully. "Besides, dying is not the same as quitting. It's not within your control."

Randy looked irritated, then thoughtful. Then, he smiled.

I then realized I had become quite worked up.

"You know," Randy observed, "You have a strange way of making me feel I'm wrong while at the same time not persuading me that you're right."

I walked to the window. Looking outside, my eyes took in the white of the birch bark, the yellow of the leaves, the blue of the sky, the green of the lawn. All the colors seemed so pure, so intense. I wondered what this world would be like without Randy. I was sure the colors would be a bit dull, a little grayer.

I felt uneasy listening to Randy talk about his death. He was talking as if it were imminent, something he had never done before. It seemed out of character and inappropriate. I also felt he was looking to me for some answers, and I wasn't even sure of the questions.

I turned back from the window, looked at him, and then asked, "Why don't you get rid of that dumb stocking cap?"

"You think I'd look better in a turban?"

"No, shave your head, Yul Brenner style."

"Yeah, right. At his age Yul Brenner looks distinguished. At my age I'd just look like a 22-year-old billiard ball." We both grinned.

Then Randy looked very serious and asked, "Ron, do you understand what I'm trying to say?"

"I think so. You recognize that you're helping a lot of people, and that's very satisfying. You also realize that there are a lot of people in need of the message you have to share, so you want your work to continue."

"That's right."

"But, you're tired, you're in pain, so you want to die and that makes you feel guilty."

Randy shook his head.

"No, that's not it." He paused, searching for the words. "I've got a feeling—actually, I know that I'm going to die very soon. As I think about it, I feel sort of relieved that the end is in sight, but I also feel frustrated knowing that if I lived longer more people might be helped. It's not that I want to die and it's not that I feel guilty. I just wish my work could continue after I'm gone."

"Why don't you write a book?" I suggested.

"A book?"

"Sure. Write up your experiences, explain your ideas and feelings. Tell people about the miracles you've seen." I then waxed theatrical. "Impart to them, my dear brother, a few of the precious nuggets of eternal wisdom that have been formulating in that balding head."

Randy ignored my attempt at humor and considered my suggestion. Then he frowned. "But I'm not a very good writer."

"You're a gifted, moving speaker. We can write up your talks and put them in a book."

"It's not the same. It's not my words that touch people, it's the Spirit. I don't think I can write what I say and affect people in the same way."

And Should We Die . . .

I thought back on Randy's remarks at the University of Utah's Symposium on Death and Dying. I remembered the sociology professor sitting behind his students. He had wept openly. As Randy said, "The feeling you have right now in your heart is the Spirit confirming the truth of my words," the professor nodded his head, seeming to recognize what was happening.

"Ron, why don't *you* write it?"

"What?"

"Why don't you write the book?"

"I don't think . . . "

Randy interrupted. "You're pretty good at writing. You can tell people what happened to me—then they'll have it from a second witness." He started talking rapidly. "You could interview me just like that reporter did. You could interview the foreman at the cave-in, and he would verify what happened. You could talk to the doctors in Italy; they'll tell you I didn't make things up. You could interview all the people in Idaho Falls."

When Randy paused for a breath, I said, "Wait a minute! Hold on. I don't know that I'm the person to write this up. It needs to come from you."

"It will. It will come from me!" Randy instantly returned to his former level of excitement. "I'll tell you what I saw and felt and you can write it, but you can also talk to other people about what they saw and what they thought of it all. Then when people read the book they will know why they are here on this earth, they will know miracles still happen. My work will continue long after I'm gone. Don't you see? It will work! This is the answer!"

Randy then looked very serious. "Ron, will you do it? Will you write my book?"

"Yes. Of course I will, if you want me to. But I've got to do it my way. I've got to have editorial control."

Randy laughed, "Sure thing Bro, you keep"—he wrinkled his face like he was getting a whiff of a foul stench—"control."

"I just mean, I've got to feel integrity in the process."

Randy laughed harder, closed his eyes, and shook his head. "I hope you got more from your college education than a bunch of phrases like 'integrity in the process.' You write it any way you want. So, how do we start? What's next?"

"Can you come here tomorrow during lunch break? Twelve o'clock?"

"Twelve it is." Then he mimicked a proper British accent. "Let's do lunch, shall we?" I pulled his cap down over his eyes.

"I don't know if I'll be able to work with such an 'attitude problem,' but I'll give it a try. What the heck, it's only your life's work, and I can finally reveal to the world the secret, sordid life of my younger brother—how he ducked his chores at home, worried his loving parents, and broke his older brother's front tooth."

Randy stood to go. Using his little finger, he lifted an edge of the stocking cap off his face just high enough so that as he cocked his head back he could see me with one eye.

"Thanks, Ron," he said with a smile, "this will be great." He left my office and closed the door behind him.

I sat in silence for the rest of my preparation period watching the shimmering leaves and feeling the weight of my commitment.

Chapter 2

A Dream
in the Night

At ten minutes after twelve I heard a loud motorcycle pull into the parking lot. A minute later, Randy kicked on my office door.

"Hey! Anybody hungry?"

I got up from my chair and opened the door just in time for a hand to stick a 7-11 Big Gulp in my face. This was immediately followed by a nondescript, flattened sandwich wrapped in cellophane. "I think it's turkey," Randy said. "But it's hard to know for sure."

He dropped a large brown paper sack on the floor and fell into my swivel chair, leaving me the straight-back chair next to the file cabinet. He put his feet on my desk and started unwrapping his sandwich. "So, how do we get started?"

I thought that was a good question. "I don't know. How about if you bring your journals by and I'll look them over."

A Dream in the Night

Randy pointed to the paper sack on the floor. I picked it up and looked inside: a blue paper folder with about 30 hand-written papers, an Italian language Bible, a small black 3-ring binder with about 200 hand-written pages, some loose papers, some missionary photos of Randy in a suit standing with some people.

"Well, if I can read this stuff, I'm sure it will be helpful."

Randy smiled. His printing was precise, and we both knew I would have no problem reading his writing.

"Okay, well, maybe I should ask you a few questions."

"Yeah, sure. Okay, I Randy Lee, having been born of goodly parents . . . "

"I said *I* will ask the questions—*you* will provide the requested answers."

"It sure is easy to see why you're a high school seminary teacher. You're obviously a control freak and love bossing folks around," Randy kidded.

Smiling, I pulled a yellow notepad and a cheap Bic pen out of my desk drawer, then slid the chair closer to face Randy.

"So, tell me. When were you, my little brother, first aware that you had a special purpose in life?"

He gave a half-smile. "You sound just like that newspaper reporter from the *Ogden Standard Examiner.*"

"Well, for now I am. Don't see me as your brother. Think of me as a writer trying to understand your life."

"Gotcha. Okay, let's start again." He leaned forward and became serious.

"When did you first feel that you were supposed to do something specific with your life?"

Randy thought for several moments.

"I guess I first realized that I had something important to do with my life when I was 14-years-old. I had a dream in the night . . . "

Randy woke up. His mom was calling down the basement stairs. "Randy, time to get up. You'll be late for church." He sat up and swung his feet out from beneath the covers and onto the cold basement floor.

As he sat on his bed trying to clear his head, Randy had the sense that something had happened the night before, that something significant had occurred in a dream—a warning he must pay attention to. But he could not recall what he had dreamed, and he felt frightened and concerned. So he knelt down and began to pray.

"Heavenly Father, did I dream last night about something that is important to me? Help me to remember. Please. In the name of Jesus Christ, Amen."

With a suddenness that startled him, the dream returned to his mind. He recalled the scene and the feelings in vivid, exacting detail.

It was night. Surrounding Randy was an immense estate. Well manicured lawns and hedges spread before him. Wearing a red uniform, Randy sat in a small sentry station. Behind him was a massive, hand-hewn stone wall that stretched into the mist as far as he could see in both directions. Two torches mounted in the wall illuminated an iron gate made of thick bars. A grand wedding and feast was being held.

From time to time, people would approach the estate from outside the gate. Pulling on a cord, they would ring a bell. When he heard the bell, Randy would step out of the guard house and approach the gate. Through the bars he would receive their invitation, make sure it was in order, then unlock the gate and invite them in. Once inside, he would instruct the guests on how to find their way in the dark through the vast gardens and hedges to the grand mansion where the wedding feast was being held. The guests would thank him and continue their journey. Randy would then return to the sentry station and await the next guests.

Usually things would go well, but sometimes things would not go as they should. On occasion, after a long wait, he would step out of the guard house and peer toward the gate just in time to see some people pulling again on the cord. The bell was not ringing. In great frustration, they would leave the gate and walk off into the night. Randy would run to the gate and call after them. But it was too late. They were gone. Upon examination, he would discover a disconnect between the cord and the bell. When people had pulled on the cord, the bell had not rung. Shocked and saddened, he would wonder how many people had come to the gate, pulled the cord, gotten discouraged when no answer came, then turned and disappeared into the darkness.

Other times, Randy would tire of waiting, take off his dress coat and boots, lean the chair against the wall, relax, then fall asleep. Hearing voices, he would jerk awake, quickly dress, then run to the gate just in time to see the people wander off into the night. He would call after them but get no response. Again he would be left wondering how long they had waited before leaving, and how many others he had missed while asleep. The most frustrating times were when he would start to daydream and become totally oblivious to the bell and the calls of the people for assistance.

Randy was confused and troubled by the dream. He was not sure what it meant but could not shake the feeling that it was in some way a warning—a personal warning.

Randy said another prayer. "Heavenly Father, I feel that this dream is somehow a warning, but I don't know what it means.

Please, let me know what I am being told. Is this dream a message from Thee? I ask this prayer in the name of Jesus Christ, Amen."

Randy continued to kneel, trying to understand. He tried to clear his mind, to be open to any ideas. Then he was filled with a surety. One moment he was struggling to understand, and in the next he knew with certainty the meaning of his dream.

He felt the Lord was telling him that he had a special calling—a special purpose on this earth. He felt his Heavenly Father was using this dream to reveal Randy's mission in life.

Randy realized the vast estate represented the kingdom of God. The massive wall showed there was no way into the kingdom of God except through the gate. The iron gate represented the entrance into God's kingdom. However, people could enter the kingdom and still not make it to Heavenly Father's presence, they could get lost on the grounds in the gardens and hedges. The grand mansion in Randy's dream represented the presence of God. And joining the wedding feast symbolized enjoying the presence of God forever.

Randy realized that his purpose on earth was to invite people into God's kingdom and to point out the way to his presence. Randy also realized the warning in his dream. At this point, he was not prepared to accomplish his mission. Like the cord which was disconnected from the bell, if Randy was not worthy the Spirit could not prompt him to touch people's lives. And Randy's being asleep or not dressed represented being slothful or not ready—through ignorance or unwillingness—to serve the Lord's purposes. The consequences of Randy not being prepared or being unwilling to serve would be people not finding their way into the kingdom or wandering in the darkness longer than they should have to wander.

Randy asked Heavenly Father to help him be valiant, and he vowed to prepare himself to fulfill his mission.

A Dream in the Night

Over the next six months, Randy searched the scriptures regularly—not just trying to pick out the story line, but sincerely trying to understand what was being conveyed. Randy listened for the voice of the Lord and prayed with a new sense of urgency and purpose. He asked for help in his efforts to prepare.

Six months after his dream, Randy began to wonder what the Lord thought of his efforts. Hoping for a clue, he asked his parents for their permission to get his patriarchal blessing. They agreed that he should and scheduled an appointment with the bishop for an interview. Bishop Sanders talked with Randy for several minutes and confirmed that Randy was worthy to get the blessing. The bishop then wrote up a recommend, informing Patriarch Melvin G. Wood that Randy was worthy to receive his Patriarchal blessing. Randy called for an appointment. Patriarch Wood suggested that they meet in two weeks. Though Randy's father was sick and would not be able to attend, he insisted that Randy go ahead.

On January 17, 1971, Randy and his mom drove to the east side of their hometown in Clearfield, Utah. She stopped the car in front of an attractive, red brick home. Randy was excited and a bit apprehensive. He had been fasting since the previous day to prepare himself, and he hoped he was in tune with the Spirit.

Patriarch Wood welcomed them at the door. He smiled and shook Randy's hand. He was an older man, well into his sixties, Randy thought. The patriarch, Randy, and Randy's mother all took seats in the living room and chatted for a few minutes about Randy and about his father's health. Then the patriarch asked Randy if he knew the purpose of a Patriarchal blessing.

Randy nodded.

"And what is that?" inquired Patriarch Wood.

"To tell me what tribe of Israel I'm from and tell my future," Randy responded.

"Well, yes. Its purpose is to declare your lineage and pronounce any blessings the Lord would like you to have. And who gives the blessing?"

"You do."

"No, the Lord does, through me. I'm an instrument in his hands—I'm his mouthpiece."

Randy fidgeted. He knew this already. He wanted to get on with it.

"Are you ready?"

"Yes," said Randy.

The Patriarch invited Randy and his mom into an adjoining room. Patriarch Wood introduced his wife and explained that she would be recording the blessing on a tape recorder so a transcript could be typed and sent to Randy later. Sister Wood started the bulky reel-to-reel recorder.

The patriarch motioned to a chair in the center of the room and invited Randy to be seated. Randy's mother sat on a chair at the room's edge. Patriarch Wood then placed his hands on Randy's head and began the blessing.

"Randy Lee McMillan, in the name of Jesus Christ and by and through the power and authority of the Holy Melchizedek Priesthood, I lay my hands on your head and give you a Patriarchal blessing. This blessing should be a light in your life, that if followed, will guide you down the paths of righteousness. It will also be a comfort to you as you travel the highway of life."

Patriarch Wood then announced that in his pre-mortal existence, the Lord was mindful of Randy and knew that he would honor the priesthood and would be willing to raise his voice in defense of the gospel of Jesus Christ. For this reason, Randy had

A Dream in the Night

been withheld until this, the last dispensation of the fullness of times. Randy was blessed that in due time he would receive the higher priesthood. The patriarch then made a statement that struck Randy as a confirmation of the special dream he had experienced.

"Being faithful to the Priesthood, you shall be called to positions of leadership and of trust in helping to direct the work of the Lord and influence the lives of others, guiding them, and pointing the way they should live to gain eternal salvation."

The blessing continued and was quite lengthy. Though Randy tried to concentrate on what was being said, his mind kept racing back to the thought that he would "influence the lives of others, guiding them, and pointing the way they should live."

The blessing closed with Patriarch Wood saying, "These blessings I bestow upon you according to your faithfulness, and I do it by and through the authority of the Holy Melchizedek Priesthood and in the name of Jesus Christ, Amen."

He took his hands off Randy's head, then walked around the chair to face him. "You're a very special boy. I challenge you to be worthy of that blessing."

On the way home, Randy reviewed the blessing with his mom. They were each impressed by a different part, and Randy was anxious to get the transcript and read every word.

The transcript arrived in the mail a month after the blessing. Typed single-space, it filled a legal size page and part of another. Randy took it to his room and read it several times. He then dug the blessings of his older brother Ron and his older sister Melba out of the file drawer and laid all three blessings on the kitchen table side-by-side. Each of them had received their blessings from Patriarch Wood. As Randy read and compared the three blessings, he noticed that although each was unique, there were also similar blessings mentioned in Ron's and Melba's that were absent from his own blessing.

Both Ron and Melba were blessed with parenthood; they would have a posterity. Randy's blessing was noticeably lacking in any mention of children or offspring. Also, Ron's blessing read, "You have been born of goodly parents, and they have taught you the way of life and salvation, by honoring them, thy days will be long upon the earth."

Melba's blessing had a similar statement promising that her days would be "long upon the earth." The only statement in Randy's blessing about the longevity of his life was very different. It read, "Continue to honor your parents and the Lord will extend your days upon the earth, to the fulfilling of the full measure of your creation, and of your mission in life."

Randy was puzzled by the differences and wondered what they meant. He re-examined the distinct aspects of each blessing and noticed a curious promise in his blessing: "Peace will be yours, wisdom and understanding; and with the accompaniment of the Higher Spirit, you shall be able to fulfill your righteous desires on the earth."

"It'll be exciting to see what happens," he thought.

Randy read and re-read his blessing and pondered its prophetic statements, each time pausing on the words "according to your faithfulness." He resolved that he would be faithful.

Chapter 3

The Pig Man

It was getting late. Spread on the kitchen table before me was Randy's high school yearbook, his school pictures from junior high and grade school, a box of family pictures, a batch of letters he had written to me over the years, and a clean white sheet of paper.

As my wife passed me on the way to our bedroom, she kissed me on the forehead and said, "I'm going to turn in. Don't stay up too late."

The clean white paper remained that way for another hour before I picked up the pen and tentatively began to write about Randy's childhood.

Beverly wrapped the blanket tight around the newborn to protect him from the February cold. She was taking home a baby boy, Randy Lee. He was born in Ogden, Utah, on February 1, 1956. His birth had been just as miraculous as the births of her other children. A squirming, crying body had been borne of her own: his little hands, his wrinkled skin, the blood, the pain, the love—an incomprehensible moment that was marvelously fulfilling.

Howard's protective arm guided mother and child through the deep snow and into the car. The Dee Hospital was soon left behind as the car carried the happy trio south along Harrison Boulevard. To the left, the snow-covered Wasatch Mountains disappeared into the heavy, overcast sky. In the distance to the right, the dark, black waters of the Great Salt Lake contrasted sharply with its white, icy shoreline. They passed Weber State College, a few empty fields, and then wound through thick, bare oakbrush. They followed the road as it plunged into the Weber River bottoms, crossed the river and climbed back into the foothills. They passed the turn-off to Hill Air Force Base, passed Hobb's Hollow and just before reaching Adam's Canyon, they turned down Cherry Lane. As the familiar barns and fences filed by, Beverly felt glad to be going home. They pulled into the driveway and sat looking at their little home. It was a four-room "basement house" that Howard had built himself. He had dug a basement foundation, poured a cement floor, then poured the cement sides three feet above the ground with the window bottoms at ground level. He then roofed it over, planning to build a house on top of this basement when they could afford it. It had a living room, kitchen, two bedrooms, and a bathroom, and curtains hung in the doorways for privacy. It was humble, but cozy. It was home.

A moment later, Randy was inside being smothered by wet kisses from his two brothers (Dennis and Ronnie) and his two sisters (Diane and Melba). Soon, friends and family were crowding through the tiny home kissing the mother and holding the baby.

The Pig Man

In Randy's second year, the family moved to a rural area between Layton and Kaysville called Fiddler's Creek. There they bought a larger four-room house above ground, with a coal furnace and a garage. The house was separated from Rosewood Lane by the creek, a wide gully, and lots of trees. It was connected to the lane by a long, gravel driveway. Their new home was situated on three and a half acres, which Howard and Beverly immediately began to improve. They fenced in a pasture, built a cinder block barn and chicken coop, erected a pig-pen and some rabbit pens, planted an orchard and a large garden, and bought some animals. Their "spread" eventually included chickens, turkeys, rabbits, pigs, dogs, cats, a milk cow, a steer, and an occasional lamb. In 1958, another son, Danny, joined the ranks, and four years later Blake was born and completed the family. The McMillan tribe numbered seven children: five boys and two girls.

To make ends meet, Howard worked hard editing technical manuals at Hill Air Force Base. He also worked various part-time jobs to supplement his income once selling Watkins Brothers products (vanilla extract, vitamins, salves, etc.), and another time tending a gas station. Meanwhile, Beverly put in 24 hours a day changing diapers, scrubbing, cooking, canning, kissing away hurts, and inventing games to cure the children's boredom.

Fiddler's Creek flowed with adventure. Randy loved the snow-fed mountain stream that was home for the frogs and muskrats. He was always excited when a farmer would plow up an Indian grinding stone, a battle axe, or an arrowhead. He was awed by the birth of calves and puppies. He even felt secretly proud when his mom scolded him for his long solitary treks up "Muddy Lane" to "see something different."

Several families, who became friends of the McMillans, lived along the creek—the Fraughtens, the Talbots, the Wiggles, and the

Morgans. These families had several children the age of Ronnie and Melba and Danny, but there weren't any kids that were Randy's age. He would often play with Ronnie and Melba and their friends, but just as often he would get left behind. A typical summer day for "the group" consisted of playing in the granary—a two-story log structure above Muddy Lane. The instant the idea was suggested, the children began a hurried, happy walk along the lane. By jogging, Randy could keep up with the others, but midway, fatigue slowed him to a walk. He would fall further and further behind, but he wouldn't ask the group to slow down. He contented himself with the knowledge that he knew their destination. He would arrive at the granary quite a while after the older children; then, because the stairs were too far apart for him to climb, he would sit on the ground floor and listen to the others play on the floor above him. When the group clamored down the stairs and out the door to return home, Randy kept up as long as he could. He would inevitably fall behind and arrive home much later than Ronnie or Melba. He was never intentionally excluded, but when caught up in their play, his brother and sister were not very mindful of him. His play began to be more in solitude than with others. Randy would go down to the creek and dig up red clay from underneath the grassy banks. He would work out the rocks and pebbles, then spend hours molding vases and animals. With a toothless grin, white tousled hair, and clay-covered overalls, he would present his treasures to an appreciative mother. Sometimes he became a stalking Gosiute brave crawling along the ditch-banks to watch a nesting pheasant or hiding-out in the haystack to spy on his working, "white man" father.

One Saturday morning, Randy was awakened by the jostling of drawers as Melba and Ronnie hurriedly dressed.

The Pig Man

"Hurry, Randy. The pig man's coming! He'll be here in a few minutes!"

"Who's the pig man?" Randy asked, rubbing the sleep from his eyes.

"He's the guy who kills the pigs." Ronnie and Melba tore out of the bedroom.

Randy squirmed into his Levis, yanked on his black canvas shoes (without socks), and pulled a T-shirt over his head as he ran into the kitchen. Beverly was fixing breakfast.

"Mom, who's the pig man?"

"He's the man who butchers our meat for us."

"Is he going to kill the pigs?"

"No, he's going to get the steer ready for the deep freeze."

"Why?"

"So we'll have some meat to eat, like hamburgers and steaks and roasts."

"How will he get him ready?"

Beverly wiped her hands on her apron, pulled out the kitchen chair, and sat down. She lifted Randy on the table, turning him to face her.

"Randy, the man will shoot the steer with a rifle; then, he'll skin it and clean it out. He'll take the meat to the locker, and they'll cut it and wrap it and we'll put it in the deep freeze. Then we'll have some meat to keep our bodies strong."

"Will it hurt him?"

"He will die very quickly. You don't have to watch. Why don't you stay in the house and help me get breakfast ready?"

"No. I wanna see it."

Beverly lifted Randy down, and he walked outside with the others.

Soon, a green pickup truck clattered up the driveway. It had a metal frame attached to the bed holding a rack that was interwoven with ropes, meat hooks, and chains. Hanging out the back, the arms of a bulky hoist swayed as the truck stopped. A stocky man in rubber boots jumped out and greeted Howard with a warm handshake. They seemed to be good friends. Howard pointed to the pasture and the gate, and then climbed on the running board as the truck rattled to the gate. Ronnie, Melba, and Randy ran behind. Howard locked the milk cow in the barn and then found the steer under some box-elder trees and led it to the gate with a bucket of grain. He poured the grain in a heap on the ground and stood by the fence.

The steer was a two-and-a-half year old, black and white Holstein with large, dark eyes and a white diamond on its forehead. Its back stood as tall as Howard's shoulder. It swished its tail and, in between mouthfuls of grain, watched the activity around the truck.

Randy watched through the fence as the pig-man opened the gate and walked up to the steer. He opened the bolt of his rifle and slid in a .22 shell. He closed the bolt and raised the rifle to his shoulder. Randy gripped the fence hard. The steer raised its head and eyeballed the stranger. A sharp crack sounded in Randy's ears. He flinched. The steer instantly dropped to it front knees, moaned softly, and fell on its side. Its legs twitched, then were still. The man gently prodded the steer with the butt of his rifle; then, satisfied that the animal was dead, he climbed into the truck and backed through the gate to the steer.

Ronnie and Melba walked up to the body and Randy followed hesitantly. Ronnie and Melba gently stroked the steer's wither.

"Go ahead, Randy, touch it. It's dead."

Randy touched the black hair on the neck, then patted it with his hand. It felt soft. It felt just the same as when the steer was alive.

The Pig Man

He looked at the red discoloration on its white forehead—a tiny hole and a spot of blood. Randy's brow furrowed. He touched the muzzle, which was still wet. He gripped the horn—blunt, rough, hard. He tried to understand. A moment ago, it was a moving, hulking animal with a swishing tail and blinking eyes, and now it lay crumpled on the pasture grass. It did not move. It made no sound. The contrast weighed heavily on Randy's mind, and he felt a little numb, a little frustrated. It was like trying to assemble a puzzle with pieces that didn't seem to fit.

The children backed away as the man swung the hoist around and lifted the bulky animal. Then, with the efficient motions of a professional, he skinned, cleaned, and sectioned the steer. He wrapped the heavy halves in cheesecloth and lowered them into the truck. He washed his hands in the trough, received Howard's thanks, and was gone—his truck clattering down the driveway.

As Beverly called the family to breakfast, Randy stood staring at the blood and wetness on the grass, and the half-eaten pile of grain.

The older Randy got, the more responsibilities he was given. His mother put a chart on the wall by the refrigerator listing the chores to be done, then rotated the jobs each week among the children. Washing the dishes, cleaning the fixtures, straightening the bedroom, sweeping the garage, watering and feeding the animals, gathering eggs, weeding the garden, and helping dad irrigate were the daily chores that earned each of the little helpers an allowance of 25¢ a week. Ronnie and Melba gladly shared their chores with Randy, and he gladly took them on. It made him feel a part of things.

The McMillans often held family nights. This was a meeting of the family in their own home. It was a time of togetherness which consisted of a discussion of gospel principles and family problems, games, fun, and refreshments. It was opened and closed with prayer. Randy loved family nights. It was one of the few times during the week when the family's undivided attention was on one another.

The McMillans also asked a blessing on the food at every meal and knelt every evening around the dinner table for family prayer. Howard would call on a different member each evening so that each member of the family had a turn. And before going to bed, everyone said individual prayers.

Through weekly religious meetings, prayers, and family nights, Randy received a thorough understanding of the Church of Jesus Christ of Latter-day Saints, its history, and the gospel it advocated. Because of this, he would never, throughout his life, doubt that God existed or that Jesus Christ was the Savior of his children on the earth.

By the time Blake was born in 1963, their little house on Fiddler's Creek was busting at the seams. They needed a larger home, but that meant a higher monthly payment. Beverly accepted a position at Candy Campus, teaching preschool children. Howard checked with a few companies and found that his skills in technical writing were eagerly sought. He accepted an offer from Marquart, a company with a government contract for work on the Bomarc missile. He enjoyed the work and his fellow workers and was happy with the change.

Howard and Beverly began looking for a lot on which to build a home with the features they wanted. Their search led them five miles north to Clearfield, where they found an acre on a road named 1000 West which would suit the family well. They bought the lot and arranged for a contractor.

As an October wind chilled the valley, the McMillan's new home was finally completed. The buff-colored brick house featured three bedrooms, two bathrooms, a modern kitchen (with range, dishwasher, and snackbar), a stone-hearthed fireplace in a large living room, a full basement, and a double garage. It even had a gas furnace that didn't need stoking. It seemed like a palace to the children, and the family felt spoiled by the roominess.

Though the children missed Fiddler's Creek, they were excited by the change in scenery. From their front porch looking west, they could see the Great Salt Lake, Antelope Island, Fremont Island, Promontory Point, and the farms and fields filling in the space in between. From the back porch, the panorama of the Wasatch range stretched from Mt. Ben Lomond north of Ogden, to Lone Peak south of Salt Lake City. It was easy to call their new place "home".

On Randy's first day of high school, he was a bit overwhelmed. With over 1500 students, Clearfield High seemed more like a city than a high school. He was sent to the office to clear up some registration problems. The lady at the desk asked if he was related to Ron and Melba. When he said yes, she turned to a teacher standing nearby and said, "Hey, you want to meet another McMillan? This is Randy McMillan, he's Ron and Melba's brother."

The teacher smiled and said, "If you are half the person that your brother and sister are, you'll be a great success here at Clearfield High."

As Randy left the office, he sighed. He was afraid that he would never measure up to Ron and Melba.

Throughout his sophomore year, Randy hardly ever saw Melba. They would ride to school together in the family's green rambler (christened "The Hobbit"), but then she would melt into Clearfield High's mass of students. He rarely saw her until evening, when her cheerleading practice and his football practice was over. On those few occasions when he did see her at school, she was always surrounded by friends. She seemed very popular. At pep assemblies and games, he was proud as she led the other cheerleaders. She was graceful and confident and beautiful. He liked being her brother.

Toward the end of the first term, Randy got a note from the office. Coach McBride wanted Randy to report to the gym. Randy was a bit worried, but he could not recall having done anything that could get him into trouble with McBride, so he dropped by between classes.

He knocked on the coach's door and a voice invited him to come in. Randy opened the door. The coach looked at him for a moment, seeming to size him up. He then smiled and said, "You've grown since I met you at Ron's matches." Randy grinned. "I just wanted to make sure you were planning on wrestling with us." Randy nodded. "Good, we'll be starting just as soon as the football season is over and I'll be expecting you to join us."

"You can count on it," Randy replied.

"Ron was region champion his senior year. Can you do as well?" the coach chided.

"You can count on that, too," Randy said with conviction.

Randy's sophomore wrestling season was sprinkled with wins and losses, but he learned a lot and was pleased when the mirror began to reveal bulges on his arms and chest that were not there when the season began.

During Randy's junior year, he performed with the school band and several choirs, made the scholastic honor roll, had a good football season, and went the entire junior varsity wrestling season with only one loss. He felt successful and was well liked.

The Pig Man

Toward the end of the school year, with the encouragement of several students, Randy began to seriously consider running for a student body office. A few days before a decision had to be made, he was asked by one of the Seminary teachers to meet with the high school Seminary faculty. Each of the four men knew him from their classes and various Seminary functions. They asked him to be student body Seminary President for the following school year. His job would be to preside over the Seminary Council and help in planning and conducting the social and learning activities for the Seminary's 800 high school students. It would take a tremendous amount of time and, therefore, would not be compatible with a student office. Though Seminary President was not a limelight position, Randy remembered his dream about serving others and accepted the position without hesitation.

In July, Randy took his traditional trip to Red Castle. When he was 11 years old, Ron allowed him to join in on the annual pilgrimage. Ron, Melba, and some friends would backpack eleven miles into the high Uinta mountains for a week. They would set up camp at the base of the massive, awe-inspiring rock formation called Red Castle. From their base camp they would pursue a different adventure every day: summiting one of the 13,000 foot peaks, swimming in one of the many lakes, fishing by hand, cooking, singing, telling stories. Since his first time, Randy had made the hike every year.

In the summer between his junior and senior year, he led the expedition. With Diane and Dennis married and busy with their families, Ron on his mission, and Melba attending college in Oahu, Randy was now the oldest at home. He willingly took charge. His younger brother Danny and a few friends joined him and kept the

McMillan tradition alive. Randy deeply believed that Red Castle was the most beautiful place on earth.

Throughout his senior year, Randy was something of an enigma to the other students. He was very popular, but had no close friends. He hung around with a lot of different groups instead of just one circle of friends. He was particularly mindful of those students outside the mainstream and would often walk past the more popular groups in the cafeteria to sit by someone who was sitting alone. In the halls, he would strike up conversations with students who seemed down or lonely. He even missed class on occasion to talk through a problem that seemed especially important to someone.

When the wrestling season began, Randy and an excellent wrestler named Stan were voted the team captains. Randy was determined to be an example in all aspects of training and performing. He developed a low-key leadership style, using a pat on the back or a word of encouragement to motivate a discouraged teammate. In addition to the responsibilities of team captain, Randy was also motivated to be an example to his sophomore brother, Danny. Randy knew that Danny was impressionable and would pick up both good and bad training habits from the team. He worked hard to model self-discipline and good sportsmanship.

Randy would often sit in class and write the name of each varsity wrestler on a sheet of paper, then beside that name he would write what weakness needed strengthening in order to improve the wrestler's performance:

Kevin - Endurance
Artie - Counter moves

The Pig Man

Keith - Temper
John - Basics
Stan - Knees
Steve - Endurance
Terry - Aggressiveness
Jake - Self-discipline
Doug - How do you improve perfection?
Pete - Keep off heels
Gary - Confidence
Chuck - Stance

He would always add a name to the bottom of the varsity list:

Danny McMillan - Tremendous energy and strength, needs to think through his moves.

At practice, Randy would make an effort to work with as many wrestlers as he could.

The team grew close. A diverse group of guys became a close-knit team that spent a lot of time together both on and off campus. Randy was drawn-in by the developing camaraderie and loved the feeling of belonging. But as he spent more time with the guys, he grew uncomfortable with the profanity, vulgar stories, and sexual exploits touted by some of the guys. Sometimes he would voice his concern and other times he would withdraw. Randy began to feel that his close involvement with some of the guys could bring disappointment and distraction, so he began to spend much of his spare, noncommitted time alone. As the season progressed, the wrestlers grew to respect Randy for his prowess on the mat and his moral stance—though some saw him as aloof.

And Should We Die . . .

Randy was a powerful wrestler with good speed, but his tenacity was what made him successful. He would not give up or give in. He was always pushing, giving 100 percent effort. Often his victories were come-from-behind wins in the last round. Another thing that was distinctive about Randy's wrestling career was how frequently he got a bloody nose. He only finished two matches his senior year without his face and the mat needing to be cleaned up. His teammates started calling him "Bleeder."

The team won five of their eight pre-season meets, then blasted through their league meets undefeated and untied. In the region tournament, Randy won every match and was awarded a gold medal as the 148-pound class region champion.

After high school graduation, Randy decided to keep a journal, and he began it with the following entry.

"My senior year at Clearfield High, I held the following positions: Student Body Seminary President, Vice-President and Student Conductor of the Concert Band, Usher Squad Captain, Wrestling Team Captain, Boy's State Association Representative, Coach and Captain of the Soccer Team.

I received the following honors: Region II 148-pound champion, letterman in wrestling and football, scholastic honor roll, voted most preferred man by the Girl's Association, voted Senior Cotillion King by the Senior class, voted Boy's State President by the delegates of the Utah High Schools, voted the most friendly Senior guy."

Randy was proud of these many accomplishments, but his most cherished honors were the messages written by his friends in his yearbook. Instead of the "roses are red" rhymes and the usual wisecracks which filled the books of his classmates, the comments to Randy's book were very personal:

" . . . I really appreciate your testimony and the great strength it's given me . . . Cathy"

" . . . I've looked up to you for an example and you've never let me down . . . Ann"

" . . . you've been a real inspiration to my life . . . Artie"

"You've really helped me a lot this year with the talks we've had. It really feels neat to have someone care for you. It makes me feel important and an obligation to do my best . . . I want to follow your example. Teresa"

" . . . You've been just like a brother to me, and I'm grateful to you . . . Jim"

" . . . Thanks, for helping my testimony grow by bearing yours and being such a great example . . . Lani"

" . . . you are so close to the Lord that you carry the Spirit wherever you are . . . Brenda"

" . . . for ten years, I've admired you because you have one quality that I wish I had the courage to stand up for what you believe in . . . Susan"

" . . . your testimony has helped me strengthen mine so much, and realize that my friends really mean so much to me. I hope you and I can be friends eternally. I've really grown to love ya' . . . Fred"

" . . . I have learned a lot from ya' . . . I have a lot of respect for ya' . . . Keith"

He even appreciated Gary for his truthfulness:

"Randy, I'll always remember you as the bleeder. Everything we did—football, wrestling—you were always messing up everything with your blood. And, I had to wrestle after you on that blood-coated mat. Take it easy. Gary"

And Should We Die . . .

In contemplating Randy's childhood and schooling, I felt proud of his success and accomplishments. I re-read the comments written by friends in his yearbook and was touched by the way this popular athlete, musician, and scholar had reached out to others.

And, as I looked at a childhood photo of my innocent, happy brother, I felt a deep regret that I could not wrap my arms around this joyful little boy and protect him from his future.

Chapter 4

Buried Alive

Randy had left a message with my secretary saying he was too sick to come by. So, after finishing my work, I drove to Melba's house. She greeted me at the door with a big hug. Her toddler, Brooke, insisted on some snuggles and kisses, and then I asked how it was working out to have Randy living with them.

"Great. Most days he gets on his chopper and goes to the genealogy library—he's researching some Italian families. Some days he's too sick, so he's lucky enough to have two nurses—Brooke and me. Then Erin helps out when she gets home from school."

I carried Brooke downstairs where Randy was lying on the couch. When Brooke saw him, she excitedly waved both arms like a baby robin trying to leave the nest. Randy gave us a weak smile and tickled her sides while I held her.

"Need anything?" Melba asked.

Randy shook his head.

"Then I'll leave you two to plot in peace and quiet." She scooped Brooke up, headed upstairs, and I pulled a chair close to Randy. He was covered by a blue blanket, and he looked very pale.

"Feeling pretty rough?"

"Yeah," he answered in a moan. "Feels like shredded glass inside, and every time I move it's a thousand cuts. But don't put that in the book. Just say 'Though in tremendous pain, he smiled heroically.'"

After some silence, I congratulated him on being made vice president of the Ancestral Research Center. He nodded but did not pursue it.

After another long pause during which I could not stop the tears from welling up, Randy suggested we get started.

I pulled out my note pad, pen, and asked, "When did you first experience a bona fide miracle in your life?"

He smiled, "The day I was buried alive."

As Randy pulled the leather laces tight, his boots felt stiff and reluctant—like they would rather sleep than work construction. He grabbed his sack lunch and pulled Danny out into the chilly morning. Randy shivered. He could never decide how to dress. Invariably it would be freezing until sunrise, then by noon the trench would be broiling.

Danny started the Chevy and raced the engine. Randy looked irritated. Danny grinned, backed out of the driveway, and they started into the darkness. The sky was moonless and the valley was engulfed with a blackness that covered barns and fields and made the road seem empty and unearthly.

Randy settled into the front seat and looked out the passenger window. For some reason, he pictured the pig man with his knife and bloody apron. Then he thought about Grandpa Richardson, who had died of cancer, and about Dr. Felt's son, who had died of leukemia. He wondered what they were doing now and what it was like to be dead. The car picked up speed as Danny steered it onto the freeway, heading south toward Salt Lake City.

Danny leaned his head forward and rolled it from side to side slowly, painfully. The thought of returning to the trench filled him with anxiety. He wished that he did not need the money and could go back home. Testing his limits, he raised his elbow shoulder high. Pain spread through his chest where last week the collapsing bank had pinned him, its tremendous pressure bruising muscle and straining ligament. He relaxed and thought to himself, "The first day back after an accident is always the worst. I'll be ok."

Randy flipped on the radio. The soft strains of a guitar warmed the car. "Led Zepplin, good." Randy said. They sang along for the first few verses:

> "There's a lady who's sure
> all that glitters is gold,
> and she's buying a stairway to heaven."

Randy was feeling unusually alert this morning—like his brain and his sight and the air itself had been scrubbed clean. The sleepy fog of morning had cleared from his head and his thoughts were brisk and lucid. Yesterday's fast had been especially meaningful and its effects were still strong. In some way the testimony of Brother Barlow—a member in his ward who had participated in the meeting—had melted something inside. When that humble man with misty eyes had said, "I know that Christ lives," some kind of barrier or blockage had been moved, and a flood of emotion had surged through Randy's chest. And now, another feeling flowed and

37

swelled and filled his being. It promised that today would be special—a reward for a sincere fast.

As the car left the interstate, it began to climb up the foothills of North Salt Lake. The Wasatch Mountains loomed in the eastern sky—an ebony silhouette against the ripening morning. Randy watched Danny's biceps bulge as he pulled the wheel hard around a curve. Randy secretly flexed his own and made a mental note. Danny's arms were almost the size of his, and he realized he had better hit the weights harder if he wanted to keep ahead of his younger brother.

They reached the end of the road and parked. A co-worker named Bruce and the foreman were waiting, shovels in hand. They all climbed on the backhoe, and it began rocking and jerking its way up the hill to the trench. Danny crouched over, trying to cushion his neck against the bucking tractor, while Randy scanned the landscape.

The sun's rays stretched between the mountain peaks and reached across the valley floor to touch the waters of the Great Salt Lake. Antelope Island glittered gold, and the Salt Flats looked strangely like snow. A doe and her fawn, spooked by the clatter, darted along the ridge and then disappeared over the crest. Randy began to cry—not visibly or out loud—but deep inside. He felt warm and good, and as he looked at Danny, he was suddenly overwhelmed with a feeling of love for his brother.

The backhoe was positioned at the head of the hole, and the crew piled off. Danny looked down into the trench. The steep sand sides plunged 15 feet to the newly laid sewer line. He shuddered. "This isn't a trench," he thought. "It's a grave." He looked down at his feet and asked if today he could run the story pole. Randy said "Sure," and Bruce answered "No problem." Danny began breathing easier.

Buried Alive

The foreman lowered the braces on the backhoe and began gouging out bucket after bucket of sand. Bruce and Randy dropped into the trench and started shoveling the bottom level. From the ground level, Danny used the story pole to check the pipes angle, then began searching for any cracks in the sand, or any signs of weakening which might indicate the possibility of a cave-in.

During the first few hours, they made rapid progress. They carved through the wet, heavy sand, laid and fitted the pipe, and covered it over. The morning was still young when the backhoe broke down and the grumbling foreman went to town to get parts. The guys knew if they could catch up with the backhoe they would be able to take a break until the foreman returned, so they picked up their pace.

Danny rechecked the pipe's angle, then stood about five feet from the edge of the trench, looking for cracks or loose sections. At the bottom, Randy shoveled steadily. The task occupied his body, but his mind strolled through many scenes. He thought about his high school graduation—just a few short months ago—and wondered which of his friends he would lose track of and which ones would stay close. He felt a little anxiety about going to Ricks College in three weeks and tried to picture what it would be like to be a college student.

His thoughts then returned to the fast and testimony meeting of the day before. Randy had fasted before. The first Sunday of every month since he was very young he had gone without food or drink for 24 hours. At the end of each fast, he had gone to fast and testimony meeting. He had heard members of the congregation stand and bare their testimonies. Some shared sacred, spiritual experiences, some recounted boring travelogues, and some laid open their lives and tearfully told of a difficult trial they were enduring. He too, had stood on occasion and publicly thanked his Heavenly Father for his earthly family. These experiences—the fasts and the testimony meetings—were a part of his Mormon heritage, traditions that he had not thought much about until yesterday.

Lately, Randy had been concerned about his spiritual well-being. He realized that his prayers were becoming mechanical and that a lot of his actions were motivated by his desire to please others, instead of a desire to do the right thing. He hungered for the spiritual realms others had talked about, and he wanted to know where he stood in his Heavenly Father's eyes.

He began his fast with a sincere prayer expressing these desires. Throughout his fast he read from the Book of Mormon to get in tune with the Spirit. He thought often about the reason he was fasting. He listened carefully to the instructors at Priesthood meeting and Sunday School. Testimony meeting had been the payoff. He felt the Spirit, and it left him with peace and the feeling that his life was on course. He felt he was heeding the warning in his dream.

Randy leaned on his shovel and wiped his brow with his shirt sleeve. He watched as Bruce squared off the sides, working away from the backhoe. Bruce had been a missionary for two years before taking on this job, and Randy felt that he should like Bruce more, but small irritations had developed between them and Randy had not made much of an effort to work them through. Randy watched Bruce shovel for a moment longer. This morning he was experiencing a change of heart and felt they were the best of friends. Randy turned and continued shoveling in the direction of the backhoe. He had only leveled a few feet when he heard a muffled sound behind him. As he glanced over his shoulder, the lower part of the wall began sliding in around his legs.

Buried Alive

Cave-in! Randy felt a surge of fear and panic as he ran toward the backhoe, hoping it would offer him some protection. His thighs and calves strained against the pressure of the heavy sand. He seemed to move in slow motion, trapped in a dream where tremendous effort is expended but little progress is made. Then suddenly, the north wall exploded, slamming Randy against the south wall and burying him under tons of sand. His right knee was jammed tight against his chest, his arms were outstretched, his right shoulder was cocked beneath him touching his knee. He fought with all his strength to push up through the sand, but its awful weight held him immobile. He tried to twist and thrash, but he couldn't move his arms or even his fingers. An oppressive force pushed against his face and ears and stomach and legs. He couldn't breathe. And although he focused his energies on drawing in air, his lungs refused to expand. Then pain, like a wind-whipped fire, began in his twisted shoulder and rushed through his torso and down his legs. He tried to cry out, but the groan did not escape his throat.

Randy felt himself relax. His struggles slowed, then stopped. He seemed to hear muffled voices from far away. *"They must be searching for me,"* he concluded. Then slowly the voices faded. The pain disappeared. Randy felt neither fear nor panic, only a peaceful calm. *"So this is what its like to die,"* he thought.

On ground level, Danny saw Randy moving to the left and at the same time, he saw Bruce streaking to the right. In the next instant, he felt the earth moving. Like riding atop a huge wave of rushing water that has reached the shallows and begins to curl, Danny felt himself thrust forward and down. He scrambled, legs and arms pumping and churning as he fought to stay on the surface. Beginning eight feet behind him, the whole north side of the trench collapsed, and Danny found himself spread-eagled, hand

and foot touching the south wall. As soon as the motion stopped, Danny crawled up the incline. His thoughts swirled. A cave-in! There had been no warning, no pre-emptive cracks. He had almost been buried! Danny surveyed the scene: Bruce was standing at ground level, but he could not see his brother anywhere. Where was Randy? Danny scanned the hole. Panic seized him—his brother was buried!

Danny dove to the spot where he had last seen Randy. He desperately began clawing at the sand—it was a suffocating enemy trying to kill his brother. He dug and scraped. Bruce immediately joined in, sending up a spray of sand. The abrasive granules cut into their hands and chipped their fingernails away. Still, the smothering shroud refused to reveal its victim.

The foreman had just parked at the bottom of the hill when the bank gave way. He saw Danny climb out of the trench then immediately jump back in, and he realized that someone must be buried. He threw the door open and raced up the hill. It was a precarious situation. The south wall, towering over Danny and Bruce, was cracking. Sand was spilling in on them. Speed was essential. The foreman slid down the collapsed side of the trench and began digging beside the others. Bruce suddenly stopped digging.

"He's not here!" he shouted. Bruce stood, strode 15 feet toward the backhoe, and stopped. "He's right here."

"How do you know?" Danny pleaded.

"I don't know how. But I know he's here." Bruce dropped to his knees and started digging.

Danny stared in disbelief. He didn't know whether to continue digging where he had last seen Randy or to trust Bruce's impulse. Bruce was now digging furiously. Both Danny and the foreman hesitated one more instant then rushed over to help him.

Buried Alive

The hole deepened and widened. Sweat stung their eyes. Their arms began cramping. Each realized they could not maintain this pace much longer. After digging down three tortuous feet, they found Randy's hard hat. They pushed the sand outward enlarging the hole. They dug out another agonizing foot of sand and found Randy's head. Quickly, but carefully they scraped the sand away from his head and face. Randy coughed and gagged.

"He's alive! He's alive!"

They pulled the sand away from his back to make his breathing easier, then the foreman grabbed a shovel. Danny stopped him. "Don't. You'll hurt him bad with a shovel."

"Not as bad as that bank caving in on top of him!"

The cracks in the southern wall were deepening. Large sections were breaking loose. Danny and Bruce grabbed shovels and the three attacked the sand with renewed vigor. Randy flinched. The shovels cut and scraped his legs but finally set him free. As they dragged Randy up to ground level, the south wall collapsed.

The attendant helped Randy into the ambulance and insisted that he lay down. The driver asked if he would like to be taken to a particular hospital; Randy said there were a few in Los Angeles that he had not visited. The driver chuckled and the ambulance raced to the South Davis Community Hospital in Bountiful.

Upon their arrival, Randy began coughing up blood. He was in shock, and it was obvious to the emergency staff that his condition was very serious. He was immediately x-rayed, cleaned, and examined. His medical chart began to fill-up with ominous medical terms: traumatic pulmonary hemorrhage, traumatic rupture of the lung, pneumothorax contusions of the chest, aspiration pneumonitis.

The crushing impact of the cave-in had caused his right lung to burst and had left him with severe bruises and pulled muscles thoughout his leg, side, and shoulder. He also had sand in his ears, mouth, and nose. In the struggle to free himself, Randy had inhaled a dangerous amount of sand into his lungs, which was causing inflamation and irritations.

Randy was taken to a private room and given a 12-hour rest. After that, a rigorous routine started. Twice a day Randy was strapped on "the rack." He was then turned upside-down, and the interns would pound on his back in an effort to dislodge the sand and liquid in his lungs. Every day a therapist would help him through painful exercises designed to rebuild his damaged muscles.

As his stay in the hospital lengthened, his condition became more complicated. Pneumonia set in, and hemorrhagic cysts developed in his ruptured right lung. But in the few spare moments between treatments, Randy had little time to be discouraged. A constant flow of visitors—mom and dad, brothers and sisters, aunts and uncles, cousins and friends—cheered him and brought him goodies.

The Deseret News newspaper printed a tiny article reporting the accident, and the visitors teased him about his "world-wide fame." He said it was a "path to glory" that he wouldn't recommend they try.

Slowly his condition improved. His lung began to heal. The pneumonia cleared up; but the cysts continued to grow. After more x-rays and hushed consultations, the doctors confronted Randy and his parents with the situation. He was healing well. The lung rupture had closed and was mending fine, his muscles were strengthening, and most of the sand in his lungs was gone. However, the hemorrhagic cysts were enlarging and spreading. If they continued unchecked, the outcome could be fatal. The only procedure that would eliminate the danger was to surgically remove his right lung. The doctors' recommendations were to carefully monitor Randy's condition through frequent examinations, then if the situation did not improve, schedule surgery.

Panic's icy fingers closed around Randy's stomach and began to squeeze and twist. Randy felt dizzy. For the first time, he realized the possible permanence of his injuries. In the past, his athletic body had always responded to injury by enduring a short period of painful inconvenience and then healing itself completely. But now, the possibility that his right lung might be removed and that his athletic activities might be restricted terrified him. He took a deep breath and blew out hard. He tightened his fists and said a silent prayer.

Randy was released from the hospital on Tuesday, August 13. His dad and mom called a special family council. The family was told the seriousness of the situation. They decided to hold a family fast beginning Saturday and ask for divine intervention; then, at the close of the fast on Sunday, they would ask the bishop to join Randy's father in giving Randy a priesthood blessing. The word spread quickly by phone as family and close friends were invited to join in the fast.

On Saturday, Randy reported to the clinic to be x-rayed. The results were discouraging—the cysts were getting worse. The doctor advised Randy against going to Rexburg, Idaho to enroll at Ricks College the coming Monday. He wanted Randy close by to monitor his condition. Randy argued that he could drive the 200 miles home on Saturdays for the examination and return to Ricks each Sunday. The doctor relented and made an appointment for the next Saturday. That afternoon, after the doctor's appointment, Randy and his parents ate lunch and began their fast.

For the next 24 hours, Randy became very introspective. He wanted his Heavenly Father to heal him but wondered if this was a righteous desire. He could not see how it would hurt, and it seemed that it would help a lot—at least it would make him happy. The Prophet had often counseled church members to fast with faith, but Randy asked himself, *"How does one do that? Do I believe real hard that my request will be granted or do I just hope it will? Maybe faith is saying 'I know that I will be healed' and then not doubting that I'm right."* But Randy could not pretend that he didn't have doubts.

Randy honestly believed in God. He had been taught that God is the father of all the human spirits born on this earth, and that he loves each of them. Randy felt very deeply that this was true. The doubts came when Randy tried to picture his Heavenly Father singling him out to be healed. Maybe in the eternal perspective, his lung was just not that important. *"But here and now I want to be whole,"* he thought. Randy decided that to be true to his fast, he would offer it to the Lord as evidence of his sincerity and hoped earnestly that God would intervene.

Sunday crawled by. Randy enjoyed the discussions in Priesthood Meeting and Sunday School, but he felt impatient. He wanted the blessing immediately. Even though he knew it would be best to wait until the end of the fast when the minds and hearts of those involved would be united and most sensitive to spiritual matters, he was tempted to demand the blessing now. It seemed so hard to wait and wonder what the outcome would be. Again and again throughout the day he closed his eyes and asked his Heavenly Father to instruct those giving the blessing to use their priesthood to heal his lung.

In the late afternoon, the members of the Clearfield First Ward filled the chapel for sacrament meeting. Bishop Kent O. Murdock presided. Throughout the singing and the prayers, the passing of the sacrament and the talks, Randy had a warm familiar feeling, the kind of feeling he got when the family knelt around the dinner table. The emotion was a comfortable closeness, a sense of well-being and contentment.

As the meeting ended, Randy watched the bishop shaking people's hands at the door. Bishop Murdock loved his little flock. At over six-feet tall and with broad, powerful shoulders, he looked strong enough to carry all the problems of the ward. As a young man, he had played professional baseball, and though now he was older, he still looked like he was in tremendous shape. Like all Mormon bishops, Bishop Mudock was a lay minister. To support his family of seven, he managed a Chevrolet dealership. But no one doubted that most of his time and thoughts concerned the members of his ward. Randy moved through the people. The bishop shook his hand and smiled. He seemed confident and positive; it was easy for Randy to reflect the same. He was very grateful to have Bishop Murdock as his bishop.

At home, Randy stood on the porch. He looked out over the flat fields of soy beans and corn and alfalfa. Their aroma—borne on a soft warm breeze—was the fragrance of home in August. To the west, the setting sun was putting on a spectacular show of light and color. The swirling clouds were islands of molten gold in a sea of burning oranges and reds. Reflecting this brilliance, the Great Salt Lake itself seemed to be on fire—a surface of liquid flame. Randy closed his eyes and felt the beauty.

As darkness cooled the sky, the bishop and his two counselors arrived. They were welcomed and seated. There was no formality; none was needed. Howard, Randy's father, put a dining-room chair in the center of the living room. Randy sat down. His family all took seats. The bishop asked his middle name and Randy told him. Then

Howard, Bishop Murdock, and the two counselors stood in a circle around Randy and placed their hands on his head. The bishop offered the blessing. He called Randy by his full name, then gave the blessing in the name of Jesus Christ and by the power of the priesthood.

The blessing was long and powerful. In the first few words the men commanded Randy to be healed; however, the body of the blessing gave him wisdom and advice regarding the decisions he was shortly to make about his education and his life's direction.

As the blessing ended, all in the room said "Amen." Randy stood and shook the hands of each in the circle. He was grateful. He was sure that the Lord's will had been discerned and that the blessing had been the vehicle to carry out that mandate. His mom was teary and his dad was pleased. The bishopric chatted with the family for a few moments, then left. Randy immediately began packing for the trip to Ricks College. For a moment he toyed with the idea of canceling his appointment with the doctor for the following Saturday, but he decided against it. The trip down would be worth seeing the doctor's expression when the x-rays announced that Randy's lung was healed.

At Ricks things were exciting and new. Randy settled into an apartment, registered for school, and attended the first few days of classes. He thought a lot about the accident and the blessing and was totally free of anxiety or fear. He was sure that he had been healed.

Friday afternoon, he made the three-and-a-half hour drive back to Clearfield in order to be there in time for the doctor's appointment on Saturday. He was welcomed home like a conquering hero and told his family all about his first week at college.

Buried Alive

The next morning, Randy and his father drove to the clinic. The doctor asked how he was feeling and Randy told him he felt super. He didn't mention anything about the blessing. The x-rays were taken and developed. The doctor studied them for an unusually long time, then ordered another set to be taken and studied them. He finally sat down with Randy and Howard. He looked puzzled, almost confused.

"These x-rays show the cysts almost completely gone. The few remaining are very small. You seem to be almost completely better."

Randy's face showed neither shock nor surprise. He just smiled.

Chapter 5

Death in the Desert

I finished my preparations for the next day's classes, stretched, got a drink at the drinking fountain in the hall, and sat down at my desk. I spied the brown paper bag on the floor and quickly looked away. "Let's see,." I said to myself as I opened my top drawer. "What a mess! This would be a good time to get this stuff organized," I said half out loud. That was the final evidence I needed. I realized I was in a serious state of avoidance. From painful experience I had learned that anytime I even half-seriously considered organizing my desk or file cabinets or closet, I was working pretty hard at avoiding something. I looked back at the sack on the floor, cleverly tucked between my desk and the wall. I took a deep breath, blew it out hard, and put the sack on my desk. I pulled out a small black ringed binder, Randy's journal from college.

Why was I procrastinating the writing of his book? What was I feeling—guilt, fear, sadness? Depression was more like it. But why? "Well, I'll work on figuring that one out when I get my desk cleaned out or

Death in the Desert

when BYU wins a national football championship, which ever comes last," I said to myself.

I leaned back and opened the journal. Randy's neat, precise printing chronicled events, activities, feelings and frustrations, love—and death in the desert.

It was a lazy September Saturday. A few puffs of clouds drifted in the sky's blueness. A soft, stirring breeze whispered of Fall's approach, and a warMing sun urged action before the plunging temperatures would force people indoors. Randy rounded up some new-found friends. They crowded into a beat-up, college-kid car and took off. Within a minute and a half they had cleared the town of Rexburg and turned the passing farmers' fields into blurs.

Almost immediately their destination came into view—the sand dunes. Several miles north of the campus, this massive, sprawling formation of wind-blown sand lay piled into huge mounds, some over 100 feet high. Its changing boundaries might be a nuisance to farmers, but they were a constant thrill to fun seekers. Stretching ridges and pointed dunes would disappear, reappear, reshape, and reform depending on the mood of the wind. Each visit was a new adventure.

Just before the paved road crested the hill to enter the dunes, the car turned left onto a farmer's access road. Paralleling the sand, they were looking for new frontiers. Clouds of dirt billowed up behind the bumping car, much like the cloud that follows a calvary's charge. The car slid to a stop just short of a wire fence. The doors flew open, and the boisterous army swarmed out. They fought over the fence and began rough-housing through the dunes. Running, shoving, slipping, tackling. Randy topped the summit of a steep pile and chanted his challenge:

"I'm the king of Bunker's Hill!
I can fight and I can kill!"

In mock anger, the others attacked. The average life span of a "king-of-the-hill" was 30 seconds. After that he'd be tumbling down the sliding sand—victim of the aspiring rebels. Finally, the weary warriors lay where they fell, gasping for breath and laughing. Then, with the initial burst of energy spent, the guys began exploring.

The others spread through the winding maze, and Randy climbed a prominent mound to take in the view. The earth-brown dunes rolled for miles, then abruptly ended at the lava flow. To the North, the black pumice and gray sagebrush stretched to the horizon. Looking Northeast, a forested mountain hid Yellowstone National Park, and to the Southeast, the rugged Tetons scratched the sky. A silent volcano cone, standing guard in the Southwest, had a giant "R" painted on its face—the product of student zeal. Southward, he could see Ricks College spread on a gentle ridge and below it, the small town of Rexburg.

Because Ricks is owned and operated by the Church of Jesus Christ of Latter-day Saints, it attracts Mormon students from all over the nation and several foreign countries. Randy had already made friends with students from Illinois, Canada, California, Michigan, New York, Brazil, and even Tonga. Many of them had come from communities where they were the only Mormons and were anxious to interact with other Latter-day Saints. But unlike her sister school, (Brigham Young University had over 24,000 students) Ricks was small, with student body of 5500. To Randy, the friendly atmosphere on campus was amazing. Catering to these students were some not-so-typical establishments: a pizza place called "The Sober Society" (practicing Mormons don't smoke or drink alcoholic beverages), theaters which showed only movies rated "G" or "PG," and Grand Targhee ski resort. Most popular was Mother Nature herself with all her beauty and danger, fury and serenity. The nearest city of any size is Idaho Falls, about 30 minutes away. Protected in its isolation and nourished by its ideals, Randy felt that Ricks was a Zion of sorts, a peaceful harbor where he could prepare himself for the stormy world.

Randy was thrilled with the present and the prospects for growth and friendship it offered, but the future seemed frightening. It held so many uncertainties. He was unsure of the vocation he wanted to pursue and even the subjects he wanted to study. He had always had some vague goals about college, a mission for the church, marriage, and living happily ever after, but now it was time to take specific steps in order to realize these goals and he felt confused.

He laid down on the dune's incline, peeled off his shoes and socks, and wiggled his feet into the sand. Randy began thinking about his accident in the trench—it had happened just a few short weeks ago. Somehow, now surrounded by the beautiful day, the cave-in seemed more frightening than when it had happened. He had been just a few short seconds from dying! What if they hadn't been found in time? Instead of laying on a sand dune in Idaho, where would he be? They would have eventually found his body— lifeless, unmoving. Then there would have been weeping of family and shocked friends, the funeral, the grave, darkness. Randy shuddered involuntarily at the thought. He shook his head to clear his thoughts, but a rush of questions flooded his consciousness.

"*How had Bruce known where to dig to find me? At the time of the cave-in, he was running in the opposite direction, he couldn't have seen where I fell. Bruce had been asked how he knew where I was—he said he didn't know how he knew, he just knew. And afterward—the blessing, my lung had been healed, and the cysts had disappeared. Could it have been coincidence?*"

Randy was sure it was not coincidence. He was certain that God had intervened in the natural events in order to preserve his life.

But why?

Why had he been rescued, then healed? This seemed to Randy to be strong evidence that there was some important work for him to do, some special calling he would yet receive. He remembered his patriarchal blessing and the dream he had when he was 14. He had faith that they were from God, but he did not understand what they meant.

As Randy lay on the sand, the sun warming his body, he offered a prayer.

"Oh God, I thank thee for preserving my life. I thank thee for healing my body. Teach me thy will. Help me prepare. With all my heart, I desire to serve thy purposes. In the name of Jesus Christ, Amen."

Part of Randy's decision to attend Ricks was the leadership scholarship he was awarded, but he also had been recruited by the wrestling coach. The more he thought about it, the more he realized that he did not like wrestling. It was something he had done because others expected it of him. He realized that much of his motivation for doing things was to live up to Ron's and Melba's reputations. He told the coach not to expect him at try-outs, then challenged him to a handball game. Randy had never played

Death in the Desert

handball before, but he decided it looked fun. So handball became his new sport.

Randy moved into an upstairs apartment a block off campus with three or four roommates. (depending on the week and who had someone visiting). He did not have a car, but several new friends did, so transportation was not a big problem. Randy set his goals for the semester:

1) Get straight A's (4.0 GPA)
2) Be Ricks College handball champion
3) Bench press 250 pounds and dead lift 450 pounds
4) Be prepared for a mission

Randy was used to assuming a spiritual leadership role among his friends, but at Ricks he instead found himself surrounded by young folks who deeply believed in Christ and whose lives reflected those beliefs. Frequently, casual questions turned into gospel study as students pulled scriptures out of backpacks and returned missionaries shared their experiences.

Randy's freshman year at Ricks was a journey of high peaks and deep canyons; his frequent emotional swings troubled him. Situations and circumstances carried him to an emotional high, then dumped him into a "grumpy funk." One afternoon he had a heartfelt conversation with his roommates, Chuck and Leroy, and left feeling uplifted and especially close to them. Then, a few nights later when he had to get up extra early for an astronomy class, his roommates laughed and talked and screamed until way past midnight. Randy was angry at them, thought them inconsiderate, and told them so. He gave them the silent treatment for about a day and stormed out of the apartment when Bruce ate more than his share of hotdogs. Another time, Randy silently fumed when dishes were not done from past turns and he had to do them all on his night.

For one of his classes, Randy was paired up with another student and they were given the assignment to prepare and team-teach a class period. Randy showed up well prepared, but his partner did not. The session did not go well, Randy and his classmate received a poor grade on the assignment. Randy was bummed out for a week.

Over and over he told himself, "When you depend on others, *they* let you down. I do fine on my own. When I have to work with others, I always end up feeling depressed."

Acting on a dare, Randy tried out for the "New Freedom Singers." He was not exactly sure what they were, but he showed up with over 200 students to try out. Some of the singers from previous years explained that they were "ambassadors" of the school, sharing their testimonies of God and country with the world through song (a bit *ambitious*, Randy thought). He loved the camaraderie they displayed, and it really did look like a good time, so he decided to go for it. Throughout high school he had liked performing for an audience but was used to having a tuba be his voice and his shield. Singing to a crowd left him feeling naked and vulnerable. He almost chickened out, but he thought of wrestling and decided this couldn't be too bad—at least he couldn't get pinned. He made the first cut and the second. When the final list was posted, he felt a mix of emotion—surprised, proud, and a bit embarrassed. He had to wear around a badge all day which said, "Hi, I'm a New Freedom Singer." Randy purchased his red, white, and blue outfit and immediately started 6:00 a.m. practices for the first tour. The traveling troupe ranged between 20 to 50 singers, depending on the host facilities.

Death in the Desert

They performed at schools, churches, and civic centers; stayed in the homes of families in the community; and traveled together by bus. The shows were upbeat, patriotic, and always much appreciated by the audiences.

Over the course of Fall and Winter semesters, the New Freedom Singers did concerts in Weippe, Lewiston, Orofino, McCall, Nampa, Meridian, Challis, Hailey, Carey, Shoshone, Missoula, and many other towns and cities in Idaho, Wyoming, Utah, and Montana. Before each concert, they asked God to use their music to heal and inspire those who heard.

Randy's schedule was demanding. Between the tours and practices, he squeezed in classes and study, weight training, handball games, and even a few dates.

In one journal entry, Randy seemed especially troubled. On a rare evening, he had the apartment to himself. He put his scriptures on the couch and began studying in earnest. He felt a wonderful calm and could almost picture the scenes he was reading about. A jarring knock at the door interrupted his focus. In walked a student he did not know very well—a friend of a friend. She seemed disappointed that nothing was happening at the apartment that night.

"Where is everybody?" she asked in an aggravated tone.

She almost left, then seemed to reconsider. She moved a book off the couch and flopped down next to Randy.

"So, what's happenin'?"

"Well, actually, I'm busy studying," Randy answered.

"Then you're lucky I dropped by to save you from the grinding stone." She then seemed to need to talk about everything and anything. Gentle hints fell on deaf ears, and finally Randy closed the Book of Mormon and just listened.

When she left two and a half hours later, Randy was too tired to continue his studies. He felt resentful, went to bed, and was in a bad mood all the next day. He copied a poem from his literature text book into his journal:

All life, death does end
and each day
dies with sleep.

On a bright March morning, Randy returned from classes to find a large package on the porch. He looked at the return address and smiled. *"Something from home! Wonder what it is."*

He took it inside, opened it, and wondered aloud, "What the heck?!" He pulled out a handful of green Easter egg grass, revealing an honest-to-goodness Easter basket. He lifted the handle and pulled out a large, colorful straw basket filled with pastel eggs, chocolate bunnies, and some homemade candy. Tears filled Randy's eyes and made it hard to read the simple note signed, "Love, Mom and Dad."

Randy had been surprised to see the package on his porch and even more surprised by the Easter basket from home. But the biggest surprise was how deeply he was affected by his parents' thoughtfulness.

He put the basket on the table with a note saying, "Hey room-mates, enjoy some Easter sweets." Then, he put his planned studies on hold and went for a long, sunny walk through the fields above campus.

Later that week, Randy went swimming at the indoor pool on campus. He was lazily floating around on his back when a student named Kurt Brinkman rolled to the pool's edge in a wheelchair. Kurt clicked the brake in place, then grabbed the armrests and lifted himself free of the wheelchair. Randy saw that Kurt had no legs. Kurt swung his waist back and forth to get some momentum and launched himself into the pool. Randy watched as Kurt swam with powerful arm strokes, splashed and laughed with the other students, even pulled himself rung by rung up the high dive, bouncing several times before dropping into the water.

On the walk home, Randy felt ashamed that he let little things get him down. "*I need to be appreciative of all I have and be thoughtful of others instead of being so caught up with myself.*" He decided whenever he felt himself sliding into a gloomy mood, he would picture Kurt Brinkman—happy, having fun, not allowing himself to be limited.

One evening, Randy took a student named Lori out on a date to a basketball game. To impress his date, Randy escorted her not to the student seats, but rather to the broadcasting booth.

"We're watching the game from the booth?" she asked

"Yep, best seats in the house!" he boasted.

Randy quietly opened the door, and he and Lori stepped in. Randy's uncle had already begun the broadcast.

"Good evening, sports fans. Welcome to Ricks College Basketball with Mel Richardson, on KID FM 96 Radio, coming to you live from Rexburg, Idaho where we've got a fantastic match-up between the powerful Ricks College Vikings and the Dixie College Rebels."

Without slowing his cadence, Mel smiled and waved Randy in. Mel's "statistician" for the game was his 14-year-old son, Lance.

"Hey Lance, this is Lori," Randy whispered.

"Hi Lance," Lori waved. Lance waved back.

And Should We Die . . .

"Lance is the youngest statistician in the history of Viking basket-ball—and the best,." Randy told Lori. Lance laughed at Randy's antics.

Lori and Randy took a seat at the front of the booth overlooking the court. Mel chatted with the couple during commercial breaks, then at half-time he put a microphone in front of Randy and inter-viewed him about the Freedom Singers' schedule. Randy was relaxed and had fun with the interview. After Mel was done with Randy, he turned the microphone to Lori. She was startled, but as she shook her head no, Mel coaxed out an interview about her experience as a student at Ricks. All in all, it was a good time.

After the game, Mel mentioned that later that month Lance was playing in a school band concert in Rexburg. Randy invited Lance to stay that weekend for a sleep over so he could check out the cam-pus. Lance was thrilled by the invitation and readily accepted.

After the band concert, Lance's parents dropped him off at Randy's apartment. Randy introduced him around. At five feet, seven inches and 160 pounds, the roommates were surprised that Lance was only in ninth grade.

"Heck, you're bigger than half the freshman here! Why don't you skip high school and come live with us?"

Several of Randy's fellow singers dropped by—guys and gals—and Randy got some chips, Shasta soda pop, some sort-of-stale cookies, and his guitar. At his own insistence, Randy started off the sing-along, strumming furiously and singing solo:

> *I don't want no pickle,*
> *All I wanna do is ride my motorcicle,*
> *And I don't wanna die,*
> *All I wanna do is ride my motorci . . . . . . cle.*

Death in the Desert

Everyone groaned and hooted.

"If you can do better, be my guest!" Randy said in mock indignation. The guitar was passed around and the raucous college kids sang late into the night.

Randy later recorded in his journal that Lance was so excited and had so much fun with the "older guys" and the "good looking women!" Looking around at the apartment—posters on the walls, a draped sheet drying on the closet door, candles, dishes in the sink—Lance thought, "This is freedom! This is so cool!"

After sleeping until ten, Randy served up breakfast. Lance had his choice between cornflakes, week-old donuts ("If you soak 'em, they soften up"), or toast and homemade strawberry jam. ("Watch the toaster, it doesn't pop up on its own. Oh, and use the right side, the left is broken.") When they had wolfed down their selections, Randy opened the front door and said, "Let's check out the campus."

Lance followed. They walked up to the student union building, then over to the Hart building. Even though it was a Saturday morning, there were a lot of students on campus. It seemed that most of them knew Randy and waved or stopped to talk. Every time someone stopped them, Randy introduced Lance—especially to the young ladies, who were quick to tease Lance. "Nice! Be sure to call me when you turn 16." "You busy tonight?" "Hey, have you got any older brothers as good looking as you?" Lance loved it. At the Hart building, they got dressed for basketball and organized a game. Lance was on his junior high school team and was considered by his teammates to be pretty good. He was anxious to do well against these college guys. They divided into skins and shirts and as Randy pulled off his shirt, Lance was surprised by how muscular Randy was. In clothes, Randy looked kind of normal. However, without a shirt,

Randy looked like an athlete in superb condition. Lance had never thought of his older cousin as a jock, more of just a cousin. And Randy knew what to do with a basketball! Dribbling, passing, shooting. Randy was a smooth, gifted athlete.

His teammates kept Lance involved in the game, and just as it started to get a bit too competitive, Randy went into his wrestling stance. Instead of playing the ball, he lifted the opposing player off his feet, did a professional wrestling twirl (including the obligatory trash talking—something about his momma wearing army boots), and gently guided his opponent to the floor as he yelled, "Two-point takedown!" Everybody piled on. Tempers cooled and the game became a half-court shoot around.

After showering, Lance and Randy got dressed and went for burgers. Then they headed back to the apartment.

"What are you going to do when the semester's over? Head back to Clearfield?" Lance asked as they walked.

"Well, we have a big Freedom Singers tour, then I'll work the summer and save money for my mission," Randy answered.

"Have you got your call yet?"

"No. Not yet."

"Where do you want to go?"

"Anywhere the Lord wants to send me—except maybe Idaho," Randy joked.

Then Randy got very serious and stopped walking. "Lance, I want you to know something. I believe in Heavenly Father with all my heart. I believe he loves us and serving him for the next two years, teaching others, is about the most important thing I can imagine doing at this point in my life. Don't you ever forget that your cousin Randy loves the Lord. And I know the Lord loves you."

Lance smiled and nodded.

When they reached the apartment, Lance's parents were wait-ing. Randy gave them both a big hug hello, then gave Lance a big hug goodbye.

"Thanks for a great time!" Randy said, and in a lousy imitation of John Wayne, he added, "Well, pilgrim, ya' come on back, and we'll wrastle us some women and kiss us some bears."

Riding home to Idaho Falls, Lance couldn't stop talking about how a guy "so old and so cool" wanted to hang out with him—just his young cousin.

Rushing to the library, Randy thought about how his time at Ricks was nearly over. He thought through the goals he had set for himself back in September. He had succeeded in keeping his weight training regimen and had surpassed his goals, benching 260 pounds and dead lifting 480 pounds. He felt that his experiences and stud-ies had prepared him well for a church mission. He also chuckled to himself at the thought of setting the outrageous goal of winning a championship in a sport he had never played. However, in his apart-ment above his bed, stood two trophies: Ricks College Singles Handball Champion and Ricks College Doubles Handball Champion. And it looked like, by the slimmest of margins, he would earn straight A's—a big 4.0 GPA. The only thing he had yet to do was read and check off the last four book sections for his Human Relations class and take his finals. Given that these sections could not be checked out, Randy was hurrying to read them tonight before the library closed.

Randy hurried to the reference counter and checked out the first book section. He spied some friends at a table who waved him over. Not wanting to waste any time, he waved back at them and continued past some book racks to some desks in the back. He sat down, spread out his notes, and looked around.

Two tables away was a student Randy recognized from his astronomy class. The guy saw Randy, then quickly looked away. Randy read several pages then looked up. The student had his chin propped on his hand and was staring outside into the darkness. Some words came to Randy's mind: *"He needs help."*

Randy paused for a few moments. He thought of all he had to read, looked at the clock, and turned to the book again. But the thought nagged at him until he stopped once more to look at the staring student. Closing his book decisively, Randy stood up and walked over to the young man. He casually asked, "How's it going?"

"Not so good."

"Aren't we in the same astronomy class?"

"Yes. My name's Jeffery."

"Hi, I'm Randy. So what's not going so good?"

"The astronomy final is tomorrow and I've hit a wall. I don't know if I'm stupid or what, but I just don't get it. It doesn't make any sense."

"Where are you stuck?"

"Magnitude and luminosity."

Randy smiled, "Confusing isn't it? And the way the professor explains it is not that helpful. I had to get a second year student to help me with it. In fact, he gave me a chart that helped me understand it a lot better."

Randy sat down and spent the next two hours with Jeffery, and when the library closed, they walked to Randy's apartment to go over the chart. Jeffery thanked Randy over and over and then took off for more study.

Death in the Desert

Randy did not finish the Human Relations class reading. He did not get an A in the class and did not earn a 4.0 for the semester. But felt surprisingly good about missing his goal.

The last New Freedom Singers tour was by far the most ambitious: 17 days, 5 states, 20 cities, 27 performances.

The singers piled up their luggage, which was carefully stacked in the bus's storage, and the overflow filled a small Toyota pick-up truck. Paul Burkhart, one of the singers, volunteered the use of his truck and agreed to drive it throughout the tour. Everyone climbed on board the bus, and at 3:15 p.m. on the day of graduation, their odyssey began.

Their first performance was in a school gymnasium in Preston, Idaho. As Randy would record in his journal, the performance included "bad acoustics, nice audience—about 750 (standing ovation)." Afterward, the singers were introduced to their host families. They rode with their respective families to their homes for a night's sleep. This would be their lives for the next two-plus weeks.

They made their way south, performing in Fillmore, Beaver, Parowan, Las Vegas, Simi Valley, Mission Viejo, Los Angeles, and Anaheim. Singing and dancing on the brand-new stage in Tomorrowland at Disneyland was the highlight of the trip for Randy. He felt somehow that this put them in a different league—a top-tier performing troupe—not just some students from a junior college in Idaho. He knew the idea was a bit silly, but the feeling was real. And, he did have to admit, they were good. Although they were world-class entertainers, they allowed themselves to be children as they romped through the Magic Kingdom for several hours.

All too soon, it was back on the bus for shows in Palmdale, Lancaster, Quartz Hill, Hemet, Mesa, Page, Fridonia, and Kanab.

And Should We Die . . .

About 100 miles outside of Kanab, Utah, Paul was trying to find a radio station. He trailed the bus in his green truck—weighed down by the extra luggage—by several car lengths. When he looked in his rearview mirror, he was surprised to see a car quickly coming up on him. The car suddenly loomed large in the mirror, and Paul hugged the right edge of the pavement. However, the gold Buick made no attempt to pass. Instead, it smashed into the rear of the green truck at high speed. Paul careened down a steep gully, plowed through two cedar trees, was slowed by a barbed-wire fence, and came to stop in a cluster of junipers.

The Buick caught for an instant on the truck's left rear bumper and was sling-shot off the road. The car was airborne over the ravine, then blasted into a wall of lava-rock boulders, violently rolling over and over, doors ajar, metal and glass spraying, black dust clouding over the scene.

The kids on the bus started yelling.

"There's an accident! Paul's off the road!" The bus driver pulled over.

The bus doors opened and students started running—some towards Paul's truck, others seeking out the wreck in the lava flow. Following the trail of strewn luggage, several guys held onto the sagebrush to climb down into the gully. Paul was sitting in the dirt beside his truck; he had no serious injuries.

Randy climbed through the ravine and through the table-sized rocks. Wreckage, tires, and $50 bills littered the scene. Thirty yards from the car's final resting place Randy saw a body. He ran to the man and gently knelt beside him. The man had been thrown face-first into the rocks. He was bleeding profusely, moaning loud. Randy pressed his palm over a gushing wound on the man's head.

"It's okay, we're going to help you," Randy comforted.

Other kids from the bus arrived to help.

The injured man asked softly, "Does any of you know how to pray?"

As he used his other hand to apply pressure to a wound on the man's neck, Randy began to pray aloud. "Oh God, we need thy help . . . "

One of the Freedom Singers was trained as a paramedic and two were student nurses. Each took over the caring for one of the three victims.

The driver of the car had quit breathing and had no pulse. The singers started CPR on him immediately. The two passengers had severe cuts, broken bones, and internal injuries.

The Freedom Singers quickly organized themselves. A couple of them flagged down the first car that drove by and told them to call for emergency help at the next town. Some students started directing traffic, some tore up pillow cases for bandages and collected water to wash wounds, and others cared for the injured—even extracting one victim reeking of gasoline from the wreck. Still others started gathering up scattered luggage.

Twenty minutes later, the county sheriff arrived. Forty minutes after the accident, the first ambulance slid to a stop. When the professionals took over, the driver was breathing on his own. The students helped maneuver the stretcher through the rocks and carry the injured to the ambulance.

Officer Lang asked the students for help in collecting the money strewn about. "Weird work," thought Randy, gathering money off the desert sand in Southern Utah. As Officer Lang finished up his investigation, Randy helped the tow truck recover and secure Paul's Toyota. He put his arm around Paul's shoulder and gave him a squeeze. "I'm so glad you're okay." Paul nodded and watched his truck being towed away.

And Should We Die . . .

Randy and the Freedom Singers quieted as Officer Lang thanked them for their help. He explained that the Buick was stolen. Three men had robbed a store and were high on drugs (he found marijuana and hashish in the wreck). From talking with one of the passengers, he learned that they had served together in Vietnam, and apparently the driver thought that is where they were. When he saw the green truck, he started yelling and had intentionally rammed it.

"It's fortunate the car didn't hit the bus going that fast, or a lot of you might have been on the way to the hospital right now. It scares me to think what might have happened if those three had made it into Cedar City. Well, thank you for all your help. You ought to be proud of the way you handled yourselves. You saved some lives in the desert today."

Randy walked slowly into the ravine. He stooped down and poured some water from a thermos over one hand, then the other. Still, there was blood on his hands. The image of the pigman washing his hands in the trough came to mind. Randy scooped up some sand and rubbed it over his hands like soap. Tears blurred his sight as he poured the water again, washing the remaining blood off his hands and into the wet sand.

When the troupe arrived in Ely, Nevada, the leaders called the Cedar City hospital and learned that the two passengers of the wrecked car were in critical condition. The driver was dead.

Chapter 6

Anziano

"Brother McMillan, it's Randy on line two."

"Thank you." I punched the blinking light on the phone and leaned back. "Hey Bro."

"Hi. Sorry I missed you at lunch. Did you get my message?"

"Yeah, no problem."

"Earl's got the car and Melba wouldn't let me out on the bike in this rain. Heck, I think I've got two mothers!"

"Don't forget Erin," I said, mentioning Melba's oldest daughter.

"Yes, that's right. Three mothers."

"How are you feeling?"

"Not too bad. It's a good day."

"I talked to Mom this weekend. She told me about what happened in Idaho Falls with Bell's Palsy. What a miracle! It really was amazing."

"Yeah, pretty special," was all Randy said.

"And I guess, from what Mom said, there were several hundred people there?"

"Yeah, more or less."

"Well, when I get to that part of the book, I'll need to get the details."

"Okay. So what are we working on today?" Randy asked.

"Your mission. A lot of your friends from Ricks and the Freedom Singers went on two- year missions for the Church, right?"

"Yeah, a lot of them."

"Where are some of the places they served?"

"Oh, let's see. New York, Tokyo, Brazil, Australia, Germany, Ohio, pretty much all over."

"What was your reaction when you got your call?"

"I opened the letter and read the words, 'Italy, Bologna mission,' sat down, and didn't stop smiling for several days."

"Then you called Mom and Dad, and they were excited for you?"

"Oh yeah. They were really excited, and Dad said something about converting the Pope."

"What did you like most about your mission?"

"The pasta."

I rolled my eyes. "What *experiences* did you have on your mission that are important to the book we're writing?"

Randy thought for several minutes then said, "John, Chapter 13, verses 34 and 35, and a family from Aviano who lived in a tent."

On Saturday, June 7, 1975, 19-year-old Randy kissed his family goodbye and entered the mission home in Salt Lake City. An old, red-brick school on North Temple had been renovated into a training center with classrooms and sleeping rooms. Randy began the 5-day live-in program with another 291 young men and 58 young women. It was a whirlwind of meetings—lectures on health and hygiene in foreign countries, classes on teaching by the Spirit, talks on loving others (no matter what they serve you to eat), and challenges to develop a personal relationship with the Savior. He heard from doctors, returned missionaries, and from some of the apostles of the church. In one of his journal entries, Randy mentioned that he heard a wonderful talk by Stephen R. Covey, who shared that the key to effective teaching was to "seek to bless, not impress" those he would teach. He underlined this phrase and added several exclamation points. He even got to listen to the Mormon Tabernacle Choir on Temple Square.

When the first part of the training was completed, Randy and other missionaries going to Italy climbed in a van and left on a Thursday night for the hour drive to Provo. They moved into the language training mission for a two-month immersion in the Italian language. They were no longer to call each other "Elder," but "Anziano," which is the Italian equivalent. They accepted the challenge to live the language, avoiding the use of English as much as possible. It seemed as if they had instantaneously reverted to the age of two, gestures and pantomimes leading to frustrations, irritations, misunderstandings, and a lot of laughter.

Randy settled into a consuming routine: 10 hours and 45 minutes a day studying the language, an hour a day studying the scriptures, an hour and a half for meals, 7 and a half hours for sleep, and the remaining 3 hours and 15 minutes for exercising, showering, dressing, and walking to and from meetings.

On Sundays, church meetings were thrown into the mix and on Thursdays they got a break from the rigid schedule to do their laundry and write letters home. As he got used to the routine, Randy decided to add more exercise. After "lights out," he would crawl out of bed and exercise for 30 minutes, jogging in place (knees high) for 15 seconds, doing 20 "marine" push-ups, then jogging in place for another 15 seconds. The first night, he did 255 push-ups in thirty minutes. The next week, he upped the pace to 400.

Two irritants became major concerns. First, Randy found that by the end of the day, he could not stay awake in his meetings or his study. Whether he was silently reading, listening to an interesting speaker, or watching a "cultural capsule," he could not make himself stay awake. Good natured teasing from the other guys (they started calling him Sleeping Beauty) upped his motivation to stay awake, but even then, it was nearly impossible. On one occasion, determined to stay awake by exercising his willpower, he left his seat in an evening meeting and stood in a corner at the back of the room. But it didn't work. He leaned against the wall and fell asleep standing up.

A second concern was severe headaches. Throughout his life, Randy, had only experienced serious headaches a few times—and even then it was usually because of a blow to the head during wrestling or football. But now, every time he exercised, a dull ache would begin, then a throbbing pain, and by the end of his workout a piercing, nearly debilitating headache would make him nauseous.

The doctor gave Randy a thorough examination and concluded that Randy was pushing himself too hard. The mental and emotional effort all day long weakened Randy. Then the intense exercise with depleted energy caused headaches, which made it difficult to sleep, which made him sleepy by the end of the day. The doctor's prescription: keep the recommended schedule, slow down the overall pace. Randy followed the doctor's advice for a week, but saw no improvement with his energy level and still had headaches with even moderate exercise. So he decided to borrow a lesson from athletes and "play with pain." He kept exercising after lights out, got his record up to 520 push-ups in 30 minutes, and continued to suffer from headaches and a lack of energy.

The missionaries began memorizing discussions in Italian. These were lessons about the gospel they would teach to the people of Italy. Randy worked hard and progressed rapidly. In his journal he criticized some of the other elders for not working as hard and taking longer to pass-off their memorization. He felt being paired up with them slowed his pace. It bugged him.

A week before his group was scheduled to leave for Italy, Randy received an urgent message to call home. His mom answered and explained that the doctors had decided his father needed open heart surgery and had scheduled it for the day after Randy would depart for Italy.

Mother and son discussed postponing the missionary's departure. At first, Randy was deeply concerned and felt his responsibility was to be home with his family. But as he prayed and fasted, he had a warm, comforting feeling come over him. He was sure that his dad would be okay. The surgery would go well; Dad would recover. Randy shared his experience with his mom and she was comforted. They decided that Randy should depart for Italy as scheduled.

"We'll see you at the airport next week, and Dad will be pleased with your decision," his mom cheerfully told him.

Two months after entering the language training mission, Randy climbed on a bus and rode to the Salt Lake City airport. His family, some Ricks College friends, and a small home-town crowd were waiting at the gate. He gave out heart-felt hugs and kisses. Tears came to his eyes as his dad hugged him tight saying, "Everything is going to be okay. Don't worry about me." Randy nodded as tears flowed. "Concentrate on the work. Everything will be fine back here."

And Should We Die . . .

Randy waved a big goodbye and boarded the plane. At that very moment, two years seemed like a long, long time.

On Randy's first ever airplane ride, the plane departed to the North, flying over the Great Salt Lake and paralleling Antelope Island. As the plane gained altitude and banked to the east, Randy had a fabulous view of Clearfield. He could clearly see the orchard, the pasture, and his home. It looked so tiny and insignificant from 12,000 feet. He could pick out Clearfield High School, Hill Air Force Base with its long runways, and Mount Ben Lomand that he, Danny, and Blake had summitted several years earlier. The plane carried him over the crest of the Wasatch Mountains, and they seemed close enough to touch. As they crossed into Wyoming at 30,000 feet, Randy said goodbye to his childhood.

The approach into JFK airport in New York City was fantastic. The flight path carried Randy nearly the length of Manhattan Island, showing off New York's skyline. Though he had seen pictures, Randy was still surprised by the height of the skyscrapers and how many were crowded together.

The flight to Milano, Italy, began at sunset. Although Randy could see only darkness out his window, he was unable to sleep so he reviewed his Italian language lessons.

After arriving in Milano, he walked around the airport with several other new missionaries and sure enough, just as he had been told, all the signs in Italy were written in Italian. Another short flight took the missionaries to Venice, and then trains and buses took them to the mission home in Padova. The mission president, President Grinceri, welcomed them. He impressed Randy as calm, sincere, and caring.

Anziano

After some sleep and a meal, Randy received his assignment. His first area of service would be Firenze (Florence, as Americans call it). Some missionaries drove him to the train station and made sure he got on the right train. Randy studied every detail of the passing landscape, touched by the beauty and intrigued by the differences. A taxi delivered him to his new home—a small, inexpensive apartment shared by five other more experienced missionaries from Canada and the U.S. They introduced themselves to each other, then embarked on a tour of the city. For an afternoon, they were tourists instead of missionaries.

Randy walked to Ponte Vecchio over a river reflecting buildings 600 years old. He gazed at the paintings and sculptures in the Galleria Degli Uffizi, and knowing that each had its own story, he wished he had been a more serious student of the arts.

Randy was in awe gazing on the Duomo, with its delicate chiseled stone and spectacular red-tile dome. He climbed the steps of the multi-colored marble campanile to get an eagle's view of the Battistero and the surrounding city. In every direction he saw a panorama of history and tradition, of artistry and beauty. He was deeply moved by the grandeur of the city.

That evening, the missionaries set up the mostra (street-board) in a plaza and talked with passersby. Randy felt embarrassed and inadequate. He would introduce himself to strangers in Italian. Many just ignored him and kept on walking. Some would return his greeting, then ask a question. Randy could not understand their question and would apologize and begin to explain that he was just learning Italian, and they would walk on. On occasion, a more experienced missionary would join in the conversation, and Randy would listen for the next several minutes completely clueless as to what was being said. He had seriously overestimated his command of the language.

And Should We Die . . .

At 8:30 p.m., they called it a day, walked to the Pizzale Michelangelo, and made plans for the coming week. From this spot, Randy looked over the red tile roofs of Florence. The city lights accentuated the stone towers and cathedrals. Randy felt like he had stepped into a magical fairy tale. Utah seemed such a long way off.

It took a while for the mail from home to catch up with Randy. Two months after arriving in Italy, he got a letter from his mother informing him that his father had come through the open heart surgery just fine. In fact, he was feeling the best he had felt in ten years. He had decided he was going to go to college and get a certificate as a building inspector. Randy was happy and relieved at the news.

Over the next several weeks, Randy slipped into a comfortable routine. He would usually sleep in (as did some of the others), leaving him little time to study his language and discussions. Usually they would proselyte for several hours either street-tracting (door-to-door) or working with the mostra. They would take a break for lunch and sometimes combine it with a bike trip of ten miles or so to outlying villages for photos and perhaps tour a historical site. Returning in the evening, they would eat dinner, then street tract or set up the mostra before turning in. Oc-casionally, they would get an appointment to teach a person or family. Depending on the situation, they would share a gospel lesson about the Savior, or teach the parents how to conduct family home evenings to strengthen their family. Randy and his companion averaged about two lessons a week, and though the minimum standard was 60 hours a week proselyting, they averaged around 40, with some weeks being as low as 20 hours.

Randy genuinely loved the Italian people, and he saw how sincere the other missionaries were in caring for the people they served. He learned a lot by working with them. And he felt bad that he was not progressing faster with the language. He felt guilty that he was not working very hard. In fact, he thought the work ethic of the district was poor. He felt they should be working harder; yet, Randy did not speak up. He did not challenge the more senior missionaries. It was easier to just go along. In fact, seeing the sights became a way to avoid the hard parts of missionary work: experiencing rejection, struggling with the language, initiating conversations. He rationalized that some of the older missionaries were going home soon, and they should be able to enjoy their last few weeks in Italy. It also made sense that missionaries needed to "pace" themselves so they didn't burn out before the two years were up.

Slowly Randy realized that while he would always appreciate seeing beautiful statuary and famous works of art and quaint villages perched on golden hills, what he really enjoyed was meeting new people—learning about their lives, teaching them about the gospel, and watching their happiness grow. His desire to do missionary work outgrew his interest in being a tourist.

As the time approached for Randy's first companion to be released and fly home, he and Randy had a long talk. They cleared the air about irritations and disappointments and decided to make the senior companion's last week his best. They spoke Italian almost 100 percent of the time (the missionaries were in the habit of speaking English in the apartment). They woke up on time (this was especially difficult for Randy), and they kept the mission schedule. They worked hard, putting in 72 hours. At week's end, Randy felt bone-deep tired and totally fulfilled.

One night, after the departure of his first companion, as Randy was going to sleep he remembered the dream he had when he was 14. The hewn stone and iron gate of the dream looked like several of the formal gardens here in Italy. He wondered if the dream was a specific warning about his time in Italy or about his life in general. He realized that the dream was literally coming true. Because he was loafing and unprepared, they were not reaching those who needed to be taught. He re-read his patriarchal blessing and was again touched by the phrase that he would "influence the lives of others, guiding them and pointing the way the should live to gain eternal salvation." He was humbled by the phrase "according to your faithfulness" and wondered if the Lord considered him faithful. He prayed long and in earnest that the Lord would help him to learn the language and learn to teach and be diligent. He confessed his sins to the Lord, asked forgiveness, and covenanted to pay any price necessary to fulfill the Lord's purposes.

Three and a half months after moving to Florence, Randy received a transfer to Bolzano. High in the Italian Alps, Bolzano is surrounded by the rugged peaks of the Dolomites. The night Randy arrived, it snowed. It felt almost like home to him. There was a small congregation of Mormons in Bolzano, about 45 if everyone showed up. Besides its Alpine setting, another unique trait of Bolzano was that half its citizens spoke Italian, and the other half spoke German. Few spoke English. Randy and his new companion worked hard, averaging 65 hours a week proselyting, but had only limited success among the Italians and no success among the German-speaking people. The language was an insurmountable barrier.

Despite the difficulties, Randy loved Bolzano. He and his companion, Elder Kelly, organized a Christmas party for December 24. All the members turned out, along with a lot of the missionaries' new contacts. Everyone brought baked goods or homemade candies.

Anziano

Randy rented a copy of the movie "The Sound of Music," dubbed in Italian. Someone put up a Christmas tree with candles and sparklers, and they all enjoyed a simple program demonstrating the people's talents. The highlight of the evening came as everyone joined in singing "Silent Night": the first verse in Italian, the second in German, the third in English, and the first in Italian again.

Throughout the evening, Randy watched a young family. The husband and wife were affectionate and loving; their six year old, Alesandro, sat next to Randy during the movie and held his hand. Randy loved this little family and felt an overwhelming desire to one day have the love of a wife and child, to have a family of his own.

Feelings of love and celebration were so strong after the *festa* was over that no one wanted to leave, so they watched the two and a half hour movie a second time. With all his heart, Randy loved this little community. Though he missed his family, he was grateful to be spending Christmas with these wonderful people in Italy.

In February, Randy was transferred to Aviano. The previous companionship had been averaging three to four lessons a month. Randy applied his habit of long hours and extra effort, and his first week there, he and his companion taught 11 lessons.

In March, Randy was notified that he was being made senior companion to a new missionary just arriving from America. He had been a missionary for nine months. He thought hard about what he had learned about being a good missionary, about serving the people in Italy, about being successful. He thought about the traits he admired in his previous companions that he would like to acquire. And he thought about his weaknesses and the ways they irritated him and how he wanted to avoid those characteristics in himself.

His dream, the dream he had at 14 years of age, returned to his mind with force. Randy had learned hard lessons about laziness and giving less than 100 percent. He now felt confident that the Lord was pleased. But he kept reflecting on the cord connecting the gate to the bell. The cord represented the Spirit, and in his dream, though he was dressed and alert, if the Spirit was not directing him, then his preparedness would be in vain. He vowed to learn how to be directed by the Spirit in his work.

When his new companion arrived, they talked over the things Randy had learned. They fasted for 24 hours and set a goal: 15 lessons taught to people who wanted to learn about the gospel during the coming week. They committed to each other to keep the missionary schedule, keep all the mission rules, pray with real intent, listen for inspiration, and act on that inspiration. Starting Sunday morning, they attended church meetings then went to work. They tracted, looked up previous contacts, made friends, and taught.

By Saturday morning, the missionaries had taught 13 lessons, with only 2 left to reach their goal. They tracted door-to-door and met a nice couple who were interested in hearing their message about the Savior. At noon, while eating lunch, the district leader called and needed some material, so Randy and his companion jumped on their bikes to ride the ten miles to Pordenone.

A few minutes out, Randy's bike had a blow-out. They walked the bike back to the apartment and fixed it using the tire off a broken-down bike, then set out again.

After making the delivery, they were hurrying back so there would still be time to reach their goal of 15 lessons when Randy's companion hit some loose gravel. The bike slipped out from under him, and he slid to a stop. His pants were torn and both knees skinned up. He found it difficult to walk.

Anziano

Eventually, a member of the congregation who was driving by recognized them, tossed their bikes into the back of his truck, and gave them a ride to their apartment. By the time they cleaned up, bandaged the knees and dressed, it was getting late. They discussed staying in for the night, but not very seriously, as they both wanted to reach their goal.

Randy walked slowly and his companion limped to the home of a family that had given them an open invitation to drop by sometime. The family was not there. They walked further to an elderly gentleman's apartment. He had already had two lessons and wanted to learn more, but he was not home either. They finally decided it was getting too late to call on anyone and headed back toward their apartment.

Walking down a narrow street, they ran into a woman they had met earlier in the week named Mary. She had taken a pamphlet from them which detailed Christ's visit to the Americas shortly after his resurrection in Jerusalem.

"*Boun Jurno*, Mormoni," was her greeting.

"*Boun Jurno*, Signora," was Randy's reply.

"Do you remember me?" she asked. "You gave me a booklet on Tuesday."

"Yes, yes, we do. You live in the house just around the corner."

She nodded. "I showed my husband the booklet. He read it that night. He's always wondering why Jesus did not visit other people in the world—your book says he did."

"Yes, that's right."

"Well, he said if I saw you again, I should invite you to come to our home," she said somewhat shyly.

"We would love to. When would be a good time for you?" Randy asked

"What are you doing now?"

"We were heading home, but if now is a convenient time . . ."

"Oh sure!" Her face lit up with a smile. "Antonio is a shift work-
er. Now would be a good time."

The missionaries followed Mary home, met her husband, and
taught them a lesson about how Christ, after his resurrection, visited the people of Ancient America. They gave Mary and Antonio a
Book of Mormon, and the couple promised to read it.

Randy and his companion got to bed late that night. They were
exhausted, and both felt they had learned something about using
the spirit of the Lord to set goals and achieve them.

The next week, they taught 25 lessons.

Randy received a letter from home. It was from his 17-year-old
brother Danny. This was the first letter Danny had written him.
Danny wrote about his wrestling season and the upcoming state
tournament. Then he delivered the important news: he was getting
married on the first of March. Randy looked at the calendar and
realized it had already happened. His little brother was married.
Danny wrote that his wife was a student at Clearfield High School
and was also 17. Her name was Alicia. Randy felt heartsick. He had
always hoped Danny would graduate from high school, serve a mission, and go to college. Now, being married so young, Randy felt
Danny had picked a hard row to hoe. He worried about whether or
not Danny would finish school and how he would earn a living.
Randy also wondered about his parents and how they were dealing
with the news. He wished he could have been at the wedding and
met Alicia. He would also liked to have spoken with Danny. It took
news from home like this to put Randy in touch with how much he
loved and missed his brother.

Anziano

One month later, Randy was surprised and happy to get a letter informing him that Alicia had joined the church and that Danny had performed her baptism.

As the missionaries continued their 70-hour weeks, setting goals and teaching by the Spirit, they were blessed with great success. Many individuals and families were converted to the Lord. Randy felt like he was an instrument in the hands of his Heavenly Father and saw the Holy Spirit in operation. They helped a couple, who had several children and were separated and considering divorce, to reconcile. They taught a father how to teach his children about the gospel in family night. They watched as the Spirit touched lives and people were able to give up addictive habits like smoking, drinking, and doing drugs. And they witnessed love replace hate, faith replace fear, and hope replace despair.

In May, they met a young LDS man named Chip Tatum who was stationed at the U.S. Air Force Base nearby. He asked the missionaries to come onto the base and teach some of his friends. Seven of Chip's Air Force buddies showed up. Randy asked them why they came and what they hoped to get out of the meeting. After some mumbling and blank stares, one young man said that he really did not know what this was all about. He had accepted the invitation out of respect for Chip. The others nodded, and Chip looked surprised.

"What is it about Chip that you respect most?" Randy asked.

"He's honest and tells it like it is."

"He's a decent guy."

"He'll do anything he can to help you out—give the shirt off his back."

"He doesn't drink, smoke, or cuss, but he's not a 'holier than thou' kind of guy."

"He's one of us."

"He cares."

Chip was embarrassed and blushed. "Thanks, guys," was about all he could muster.

The missionaries took that sincere beginning and shared with the men the reason Chip was the man he was: the gospel of Jesus Christ. It was a lively, respectful, considerate discussion, and afterward two of Chip's friends, Dave and John, asked to learn more.

The missionaries began teaching Dave and John separately. Dave was easy to like. He was friendly and had a great sense of humor. Randy liked him immediately. Dave said that he was struggling with life in general. When he was transferred to Italy, his wife stayed stateside. He loved her and realized he had made some big mistakes in their relationship. Dave also felt restless, like there was something important he should be doing, but that he was off course and could not find his purpose. Chip felt that Dave had some problems with alcohol, but Dave insisted he had it under control. At the end of the lesson, the missionaries taught Dave how to pray. He said a heartfelt prayer asking, "Oh God, if you are real, will you please help me find you?"

John was also eager to learn from the missionaries. He was tall and thin and he did a fabulous John Wayne impersonation. He called himself "The King." After the first lesson, he started praying and reading both the Book of Mormon and the Bible—the latter being a book he had always meant to read but had never gotten around to doing. On the third lesson, he told the missionaries that he believed their message was true. They taught him about the Word of Wisdom and explained that in these the latter-days, God had commanded His church through his prophet Joseph Smith, that they not partake of alcohol, tobacco, coffee, or tea. John was very somber.

"I do all that stuff, and I like it. I might be able to go without cig-arettes, but you just can't have fun without drinking!" he seemed to plead.

"That's not all," Chip added. "Elder McMillan, tell him about pornography."

"Oh, come on guys, surely you're joking," John said in disbelief. Chip explained that John had pictures of nude women taped up all over his room.

Randy taught him about morality and how the prophets taught that there should be no sexual relationships outside of the marriage covenant.

John was sorrowful, but he promised to read the scripture refer-ences they gave him and to pray about them.

Later, as an experiment, Chip took John out to the Barufu La Strada, where they drank only Gassosa and other soft drinks. They met some new Italian friends, danced, and laughed. Afterward, John admitted they'd had a good time—without drinking booze.

On May 14, Dave took the missionaries out for pizza. They were walking home when all the lights went out. The ground started rumbling and shaking. They had a difficult time keeping their bal-ance. Then all was still. People flooded into the streets. It took a moment for Randy to realize that they had just experienced a major earthquake. Over the next week, 70 aftershocks rocked the area.

Aviano was only mildly affected—damaged buildings, but no casualties. But as the news began coming in, they realized the mountain areas had been devastated. There had been over 5,000 fatalities, and thousands more were injured or missing. A few days after the first quake hit, storms battered the already devastated area, carrying with them hail the size of marbles, torrential rain, and severe winds. The water in Aviano was contaminated and had to be boiled before drinking. Many areas had no water at all. Huge land-slides in the mountains blocked the major roads accessing the area.

The U.S. Air Force base began mobilizing a relief effort. The Italian communist party protested and blocked the aid of the United States. Chip, Dave, and John volunteered as individuals not representing the U.S. Air Force and drove a civilian truck with medical supplies, army tents, and purified water to the worst hit villages.

As the need became overwhelming, the government relented and desperately needed U.S. aid reached the area. Vice President Rockerfeller flew into Aviano to show support.

In the weeks that followed, Randy was stunned by people's reaction to the missionaries' message following the earthquake. Instead of the usual apathy, some shouted at them and ordered the missionaries off their property. He heard such things as "How could a loving God allow this to happen? There is no God and you are not his representatives." And, "If there is a God, he is a God of death and suffering. I want nothing to do with a God like that." Yet, others were humble and questioning, "Life is so fragile and can be gone in a moment. What is life for? Surely there is a purpose. What do you believe?"

As Randy was studying in the early morning hours, strong images came to mind: the pig man and the steer, the cave-in and the blackness, the car accident and blood on the desert sand. He thought of the thousands of dead in the recent earthquake. He opened a letter sent to him from a friend at Ricks and re-read five typed pages about the experience of President Hale, an LDS stake president in Idaho. This man had written the account of his own death and passing into a world of spirits. He wrote of the marvelous love and peace there and how he was greeted by deceased loved ones. He wrote about how those who have not had a chance to learn and understand the Savior's gospel on earth, learn about it there and can accept or reject it. He wrote about how in mortality we learn from our suffering and our experiences and they help us grow and love. President Hale wrote about his return to the mortal world and testified that life exists beyond death. As Randy pondered President Hale's account, he was overwhelmed with a feeling of joy and light. In a way he could not describe, he knew that knowledge and understanding had been given to him. He knew that what President Hale had written was true. He knew that, just as the scriptures testify, there is life after death. Afterward, Randy was exhausted and full of peace.

Later that day, they came upon a family living in a tent next to their damaged house. They greeted the missionaries and invited them into their "new home." They all talked about the events of the previous weeks. The family mentioned that they had lost some relatives in the flooding that followed the quake. Yet, Randy heard no trace of bitterness nor hardness; he instead heard expressions of gratitude. They were grateful to all be alive, grateful to have food to eat, and grateful for their tent.

They asked the missionaries the purpose of their visit. Randy told them, they wanted to discuss three questions with the family: Where did we come from before this life? Why are we here? Where are we going when this life is over?

The family asked them to stay and teach them. Randy bore strong testimony that before being born, we were spirit children of our Heavenly Father. That we came to earth to experience opposition and learn the difference between the bitter and the sweet, the good and bad, and exercise our free choice. When we choose good, we become more Christ-like, and when we choose evil, we become less like the Savior. When we accept the Savior's atonement, we can be forgiven for our mistakes and receive his power in our lives. When we die, our bodies go to the grave, but we go to a spirit world where we use all the sorrows and suffering, the love and the joy of our earthly experiences to grow and learn and help others to learn and grow. And after all have had the chance to learn the gospel and accept it or reject it—either on earth or in the spirit world—then comes the resurrection. Our spirits are reunited with our bodies, never to part again. We are saved from death, and those who choose the Savior are saved from sin and live with him and their families in his kingdom of love and joy.

The humble family in the tent thanked the missionaries and asked them to come back and teach them more. Randy reflected frequently on the family living in a tent. They had lost so much—their home, loved ones—yet their response to adversity was gratitude and humility. Randy felt they taught him more than he had taught them.

Randy and his companion rode their bikes onto the base to set up teaching appointments with Dave and John. Arriving at the barracks, they found Dave and John on the front steps sharing a bottle of wine. "Hey, Elders," Dave shouted, waving them over.

"Looks like you haven't given up drinking yet," Randy observed.

"Not yet," John responded, and he and Dave laughed.

"Tell me honestly," Randy spoke seriously. "Do you guys want to continue our discussions?"

Dave and John were suddenly very serious.

"I do," John answered.

"So do I," Dave said. "Really."

Randy and his companion set appointments to teach each of them.

Anziano

That night their zone leaders called. They had been praying about the people being taught in their zone and the Spirit told them to talk with Dave about being baptized.

Randy thought they were crazy, "He's just not ready," Randy told them, and his companion agreed.

"Will you pray about it?" the zone leaders asked.

Randy and his companion said they would. They got on their knees and asked their Heavenly Father what they should do about Dave. As they were quiet and tried to be open to any feelings or thoughts, Randy had a strong impression that Dave should be baptized soon or it would not happen at all. His companion felt the same.

At the next appointment, Dave was surprised when Chip showed up with four young elders instead of the usual two. Randy introduced his two zone leaders then asked Dave to give an opening prayer. Randy then asked Dave point blank if he had quit drinking. Dave said no, he had gotten drunk the night before. Randy asked him how he felt about what they had been teaching him. He said it seemed good to him, but he wasn't sure yet.

Each missionary shared some thoughts with Dave, then Randy spoke.

"Dave, I know what we have been teaching you is true. I know it because the Lord revealed it to me. He lives. He really does."

Dave felt a sudden burning feeling. It grew stronger. His eyes began tearing up.

Randy continued, "That feeling you have right now is the Spirit witnessing to you that what I'm saying is true."

After waiting nearly a full minute as Dave basked in the Spirit, Randy said, "Dave, I challenge you to be baptized into the Church of Jesus Christ. Will you?"

Dave thought for a long minute and answered, "Yes, I will." Then he added, "Elder McMillan, would you perform the ordinance?"

"Of course," Randy said with a smile.

Randy said he would arrange for missionaries to visit Dave's wife in the States so she would better understand the decision he had made. Dave hoped she would be interested as well.

They scheduled the following Saturday for Dave's baptism.

"Now, this means that from this moment on you must start living the teachings in every way, including abstinence from alcohol."

"I know, and I will," was Dave's promise.

During their next visit with John, he agreed to live the Word of Wisdom, throw out all his pornography, and remove the nude pictures from his wall. (He later confessed that he carefully cut out the beauties' heads and made a collage of smiles that he kept on his wall.)

On Thursday evening, two days before Dave's scheduled baptism, Randy received a phone call from the zone leaders informing him that he was being transferred the next day to Vicenza. There he was to be a district leader, responsible for leading six missionaries.

Randy called President Grinceri and requested a delay of one day so he could baptize Dave. The president said, "I'm sorry, no. You're needed in Vicenza." Randy was disappointed. He used Friday to say goodbye to those he had grown to love. He apologized to Dave for not being able to baptize him. Dave told him it did not matter who baptized him, as long as it was performed by one who had the authority. He added, "What does matter is that you taught me and cared about me, and that's what counts in the record book of Heaven."

Anziano

On Friday, Randy caught the train to Vicenza. Chip baptized Dave on Saturday, and John and three other investigators were baptized the following week. Randy of course had no way of knowing that in 12 months he would get a letter from Dave saying that he had never been "so happy in all my life" and thanking Randy for not giving up on him. Nor could Randy know that six months after writing that letter, Dave would be killed in a car accident.

In Vicenza, Randy tried to do his work by the Spirit. He continued to work hard, and he supervised six other missionaries. He even made a special effort to celebrate the bicentennial of America's birth by working 72 hours and teaching 20 lessons that week. And as he labored, his love grew for the people he served.

The last part of August, Randy was notified that Elder Kelly was being transferred to Vicenza and would be his new companion. This was a surprise, especially given that Elder Kelly had been Randy's companion in Bolzano. Randy was not aware of a single time that elders had been reassigned to each other after already serving together. As Randy contemplated the new change, he thought back on his former companionships and reviewed his previous mission journal. He was surprised and dismayed as he realized how critical he had been of his companions. He had expressed irritation at some of their actions, he was bugged by some of their attitudes, and he was critical of their weaknesses. Randy felt bad as he realized that he had measured them by his own impossible standards, then was disappointed when they did not meet his expectations in every way. For the most part, he had gotten along well with them, but his own journal revealed that Randy had created a barrier between himself and with his companions. His judgements had held them at arm's length. In prayer, he asked his Heavenly Father to forgive him and take this weakness from him. He asked that he might see his companions as his Savior saw them, that he might be caring and accepting.

Fortunately, this was easy with Elder Kelly, who was eager to do the work, kind and forgiving, and a lot of fun to be with. Randy welcomed Elder Kelly to Vicenza and they talked about what they had learned so far on their missions and how they wanted to do things. Then they prayerfully set their goals and went to work. Randy loved working with his "new" companion. He laughed at his banter between doors. He thoroughly enjoyed Elder Kelly's teachings. When he taught, Elder Kelly would tell jokes and be laughing one minute, then be tearfully expressing his testimony the next. He expressed his love for the people and taught with sincerity and conviction. And when Elder Kelly made mistakes in teaching or flubbed the language or complained about being stood up by some contacts, Randy just smiled and said to himself, "No big deal, the Church is still true."

Randy realized that when he overlooked Elder Kelly's weaknesses and accepted him completely, without judgements, his strengths were much more obvious and Randy appreciated them even more. Randy realized that where he was weak, Elder Kelly was strong and where Elder Kelly was weak, Randy was strong. Together they were an effective team and great friends.

They worked well together; they worked hard and had extraordinary success.

After a long string of powerful lessons and touching baptisms, Randy was feeling thankful and grateful.

"Elder Kelly," he asked, "why do you think we're so blessed? I mean, I've worked just as hard in other areas and taught just as often, but why is it that we've been so blessed here?"

Anziano

Elder Kelly replied, "The difference is that we get along well and we're friends. It's easy to have the Spirit with you when you love your companion, and the people can see the love in you."

Randy wrote down his formula for a successful mission:

> 1- *Keep the mission rules and schedule.*
> 2- *Work hard, go the extra mile.*
> 3- *Plan by the Spirit, work with the Spirit.*
> 4- *Love your companion.*

Then he added a scripture—John 13:34-35—just to remind himself: "A new commandment I give unto you, that ye love one another; As I have loved you . . . .by this shall all men know that ye are my disciples, if ye have love one to another."

After serving as a missionary for 16 months, Randy was called to be a zone leader, which meant he would be responsible for organizing a new zone and leading 25 missionaries in 4 different cities. He was transferred to Parma and reluctantly wrote his parents that now he would have a car and need to pay for gas. He now required $200 a month for his total expenses.

This new responsibility required a lot of travel and working with a lot of different missionaries. He felt even greater fatigue than usual. He had an embarrassing problem: he could not wake up on time. He would sleep through the alarm and eventually had to ask the missionaries to please shake him awake when they got up and to not leave him laying down, or he would fall back asleep. He insisted they make sure he was sitting up before they left him alone.

Randy served as zone leader for a month and started to feel like he was doing a good job. One morning on a preparation day, he was awakened by a sharp pain in his lower abdomen. It felt like a charlie horse (cramps he sometimes got when wrestling). But instead of the pain being in his legs, this pain came from deep inside.

When his companion woke up, Randy explained the problem. They talked about going to the hospital, but Randy had heard too many horror stories about missionaries in Italian hospitals. Randy decided to go with his companion to the scheduled district basketball game and see if the pain worked itself out. Randy laid on a bench in the gym while the Utah Elders battled the Idaho Elders. The pain slowly subsided, and Randy enthusiastically donned his trunks and joined in the fray.

Two weeks later, Randy jerked awake. An awful pain tightened him into a fetal position. This time the pain was in his groin, and he felt like he had been kicked by a mule. Randy called out to his companion, who helped dress him and then drove him to the hospital. At the hospital, the pain intensified and there was a noticeable swelling. Randy had absolutely no idea how to say groin in Italian, and they could not find anyone who spoke English.

The doctors began testing, taking blood and x-rays, and probing and moving him from room to room. The pain increased, as did the swelling. They gave him a shot of pain killer , but it had no effect. They increased the dosage, and still Randy felt no relief. The day stretched into night. The doctors were consulting with specialists around the country. Occasionally, they would hurry into his room and conduct another test. The pain continued to worsen.

The next morning, the doctors huddled with Randy and after repeated efforts that included drawing pictures on a napkin, Randy understood that he had a blood clot and urgently needed an operation. He came to understand that because of the difficulty posed by the location of the blood clot, they would perform the operation in steps. If the first step, which was a basic and relatively easy surgery, worked they were done. If it was not successful, then they would move to step two which was much more risky and could result in permanent damage and jeopardize his ability to have children. Only as a last resort would they move to the third step, which would cause irreversible damage, but would save his life. The doctors did not seem to be asking his permission as much as they were informing him about what needed to be done. They left Randy to himself while they prepared for the operation.

Randy tried to get a call through to his parents, but a connection with the States could not be made. He was troubled and afraid. Randy said a short prayer. When the doctors returned, they looked grim. Without beating around the bush, they said that the results of the blood tests showed Randy had leukemia. His white blood cell count was 350,000. Normal levels are between 3,000 and 10,000 white blood cells per milliliter of whole blood. They were not sure how that would affect his operation, but it could not be delayed. They said they would come get him as soon as preparations were done and then left Randy alone.

Leukemia! The only thing Randy knew about the disease was that it had killed his twelve- year-old friend when Randy was young, and that on the "Dr. Welby" TV show, he always gave someone with leukemia two years to live and then they died.

Randy crawled out of bed, gathered his hospital gown around him, and knelt on the tile. He poured out his heart in prayer. He was fearful and felt all alone. He missed his family and desperately wished to be home. He asked his Heavenly Father for help and that he be healed, then added, "But nevertheless, thy will, not mine, be done." He climbed into the bed. A tangible wave of peace washed over him. He felt calm and comforted. The fear and anxiety were gone. He no longer felt alone. He knew he was in God's hands.

A moment later, they wheeled Randy into the operating room and administered the blessed anesthesia.

In Utah, Randy's father Howard awoke from a sound sleep. He got a drink, climbed back in bed, got up again, and began pacing through the house. His movements woke up Randy's mother. She took Howard's hand and sat him down.

"Honey, what's wrong?" she wondered.

"I don't know. Something's wrong with Randy. I don't know what it is or what we can do, but something is definitely wrong with Randy."

"Lets pray for his protection," she suggested.

The next night, before retiring to bed, Howard experienced the same feeling. He and Beverly prayed again. Around midnight they got a phone call. The man on the line said he was a doctor calling from Italy. He said they had been trying to get through since the day before and apologized for the delay. He explained all the details about Randy's condition and said he was being operated on as they spoke. He promised to call as soon as there was any news and gave them contact names and phone numbers. Howard and Bev hung up the phone, said a prayer asking their Heavenly Father to be with their son, and started calling family members with the news.

The operation went longer than expected. Because of the internal damage, they immediately proceeded to step two of the plan. They removed the blockage, repaired the vessels, and sewed Randy up. But later that night he began hemorrhaging. They almost lost him before a nurse making her rounds found his bedding soaked with blood.

Randy was given an emergency blood transfusion and was rushed into another operation. After trying several procedures without success, they decided to keep the incision open—allowing him to bleed slowly—and to use IV's to keep him alive.

A little while later, Randy gained consciousness for the first time in two days. He was nauseous and disoriented and in awful pain. An apologetic doctor was repeatedly inserting a needle in an attempt to find a vein that had not collapsed.

Randy was bleeding to death. He was bleeding faster than the IVs could deliver blood. Randy was anesthetized again and the doctors operated once more, closing everything up and hoping for the best.

That night, though still under heavy sedation, Randy sat up in bed and began talking to the startled man in the bed next to him. Randy began interviewing him for baptism. The frightened patient tried to give the right answers while repeatedly pressing the nurse's call button. Randy congratulated the man on his coming baptism and asked for white clothes so the new convert could be baptized then and there. When none were forthcoming, Randy struggled out of bed to take care of it himself, knocking over the IV tree, a bed stand, and a clanging bedpan. By this time, several nurses and orderlies had arrived and settled him down. Randy never woke during the entire episode.

When Randy regained consciousness, he was extremely swollen, and as he described it, "crazy thirsty" and in "a heap of hurt." The nurses were attentive and helped him a lot. He found himself in a large room with three beds and two other patients but without TV or radio. Not feeling good enough to read, Randy tried conversation to relieve the boredom. One of the patients—not the one he had tried to baptize—was interested in what a young American was doing in Italy. Randy explained that he was a missionary for the Church of Jesus Christ of Latter-day Saints. When the patient asked more questions, Randy began teaching him one of the lessons about the latter-day prophet, Joseph Smith. The other patient in the room listened (he had little choice) but did not say anything (perhaps he was still mad at Randy for trying to baptize him against his will). Randy spotted his scriptures on the bedstand, and upon opening them found a Joseph Smith pamphlet, which he gave to his new friend. The patient thanked him for the explanation and the gift.

Randy nodded off to sleep. When he awoke, he noticed the man reading the pamphlet. The man quickly put it away when he saw Randy watching him. After Randy had taken another nap, the patient asked him several questions about Joseph Smith's life, and he seemed genuinely interested.

Toward day's end, Randy's companion arrived. Randy was so glad to see him. His companion recounted all that had happened the last five days and how Randy had almost died. He told Randy that he had spoken with his parents and they were wonderful people. "They're working hard to get passports," he said, "so they can come to be with you." He told Randy that there had been a huge snowstorm and that President Grinceri would be here as soon as the roads were passable. He ended his narrative by asking Randy if there was anything he needed.

"Yeah," Randy nodded. Then, with a mischievous smile he said in a whisper, "Can you bring me a whole stack of Joseph Smith pamphlets?"

Randy spent a difficult night in pain. His companion delivered two stacks of pamphlets the next morning and told him the mission president would probably be arriving from Padova that afternoon.

Anziano

Randy was anxious to talk to the man in the bed next to him, both to get his mind off his pain and to teach another lesson to his friend. However, the man was feeling better and spent most of the morning out of his bed walking around the hospital. Randy was disappointed, but around noon a nurse Randy did not recognize came to him and asked for "one of those booklets about the Mormon prophet." Surprised, Randy asked where she heard about him. She explained that a patient had stopped at their nursing station and had excitedly told them about a modern prophet—just like the prophets in the Bible—named Joseph.

A few minutes later an orderly came to Randy's room and asked for a pamphlet. Then another nurse requested one, then an intern and a young doctor. By late afternoon, Randy had distributed the first stack of pamphlets and was working on the second. Randy was excited about his new method of proselyting and thought, *"If the Lord would just give leukemia to all the missionaries, we could have Italy converted by New Year's."*

That afternoon, President Grinceri arrived. He was deeply concerned and had already spoken with the doctors about Randy's condition. He explained to Randy that his leukemia was CML, a very slow growing leukemia. Because of the large amount of it in his body, his condition was very serious. He added that it was likely he had been carrying it since high school. Randy immediately thought of all the nose bleeds in wrestling and the headaches in the Language Training Mission. He thought of the trouble he had with staying awake and sleeping in.

President Grinceri added, "The fact that your condition was not discovered in your medical exams before your mission leads me to believe someone must have wanted you to be a missionary in Italy."

"As soon as I get feeling better, I really want to finish my mission. I'm sure the Lord will help me," Randy stated with conviction.

The president slowly shook his head.

"I have given this a lot of thought and prayer, and the Lord wants you to go back with your family as soon as you are feeling up to it."

For Randy, the thought that this leukemia was killing him was not as painful as the thought that his mission was over and that he would be going home early.

President Grinceri put his hands on Randy's head and gave him a blessing. The feelings that came so powerfully to Randy in answer to his prayer a few days ago returned. Randy did not remember all that was said in the blessing, but he did remember the wonderful feeling of peace and calm and the words, "I bless you to live to see numerous miracles in your life."

The next day Randy spoke with his parents on the phone. It was great to hear their voices. He told them not to worry and not to come to Italy. He shared with them the blessing he had been given and said he would be home soon. They were encouraged and grateful.

Randy began to steadily improve from his operations. Just before Christmas, he was moved to his own room. Still too weak to move around, hospital employees began showing up in his room during breaks and at meals to ask questions about the pamphlet. Randy's companion joined him to teach the lessons to individuals and small groups. Several doctors joined in on the discussions, as did patients on occasion. Randy gave up trying to track lessons taught and Books of Mormon given. Instead, he treasured every conversation, knowing that all too soon he would be leaving.

Anziano

On January 3, hospital employees dropped by in twos and threes to wish him well. His companion was amazed at the number of well-wishers. Randy thanked everyone for their excellent care. Some missionaries drove Randy to the airport and used a wheelchair to get him to his plane. He needed help climbing the boarding stairs. They got him seated, gave him a big hug, and rushed off the plane just as the doors closed. The plane took off, and Randy cried himself to sleep.

Chapter 7

In the Long Silence
of the Night

Randy and I were sitting on my living room floor. Photos, slides, and letters from his mission were scattered around us.

"What were you feeling at the airport?" he asked me.

"You mean while we were waiting for your plane?"

"Yep."

"Well, I was sad that you were sick, but I was also happy that you were alive, of course, and I was really excited to see you again. You had been gone for over a year and a half and my wife was looking forward to meeting you. So, I guess I had a lot of mixed feelings."

"What did you think when you first saw me?"

"I was shocked. I honestly didn't recognize you until you spoke."

"Really?"

"Yeah! You left on your mission weighing a 170 pounds without an

In the Long Silence of the Night

ounce of fat, and when you got back you were what? One thirty-five?"

"One hundred and twenty-eight, actually," he said matter of factly.

"Your face was so thin, I didn't know it was you until you said, 'Hey Bro.'"

Randy turned pensive. "Ron, why do you think the Lord gave me leukemia?"

"Oh Randy, the Lord didn't give you leukemia. Mortality gave you leukemia," I said strongly.

"But why me? Why did I get leukemia?"

"Look, Randy, that's an irrelevant question. In our pre-mortal life, you agreed to come here. You knew there would be pain and hardships, and you came to experience and to learn. While in mortality, some people get in car accidents, some stub their toes. You got leukemia. The question isn't why did you get it. The question is, now that you have it, how are you going to respond to it?"

"I know I either choose to be miserable or to have a positive mental attitude. I know that's up to me. But why did I get it in the first place? Is leukemia part of my life's plan?"

"I don't think God sat down with you and decided you would go to Clearfield High and then decided you would get leukemia. That's not how life works. You make choices, there are consequences, there are accidents. Bad things happen."

Randy thought for a long moment, then replied, "You are a learned man, but, I think you're wrong on this one, Bro."

Family and friends nearly smothered Randy at the airport. Randy's legs gave way. The long plane ride had been very hard on him. His mom got him comfortably seated in a wheelchair; then, following the doctor's orders, he was rushed up to the University of Utah Medical Center. Randy was barely conscious when the doctors took over. They had been thoroughly briefed by the doctors in Italy and had a plan carefully laid out. After whisking Randy away to get the treatment going, some of the staff members sat with the family.

"Randy has chronic myeloid leukemia—CML," the doctor began. "Of the four kinds of leukemia, Randy has the best kind to treat. It's slow moving and is frequently managed with drug therapy. Leukemia is cancer of the blood cells. In Randy's case, the white blood cells are out of control, which means they suppress the red blood cells and don't do their own job very well. Randy is in the chronic phase of CML. With such a high count of white blood cells—he had . . . let me see . . " she fumbled through some papers and continued, "a normal, healthy person has a white blood cell count of between 3,000 and 10,000 per milliliter. In Italy, Randy's count was over 350,000. He almost died, but he did respond well to treatment. There is no cure for leukemia but lives can be extended. Our plan is to stabilize his overall condition, then control his blood count with medication. This facility is one of the best in the world for researching and treating leukemia. Randy is very fortunate to be here. Any questions?"

The discussion continued for nearly an hour. The family was grateful for the information and the caring manner of the staff.

After a week, Randy was doing well and was allowed to have visitors. A local paper printed a story about his return and condition. Extended family, friends, high school buddies, Freedom Singers, and neighbors dropped by to visit him, and the hospital was deluged. The staff had to carefully monitor his room to keep the visitors to three at a time and to shoo people out after hours.

In the Long Silence of the Night

In the long silence of the night, Randy would think and reflect. He thought about his desires. With all his heart, he wanted to be doing the Lord's work in Italy. With all his heart, he wanted to be healthy and fit. Randy thought about his patriarchal blessing which stated, "You shall be able to fulfill your righteous desires on earth." Were not his desires to be a missionary and to be healthy righteous? How could they not be righteous? Why weren't they being fulfilled?

One of the doctors had told Randy that by all appearances, he had been in the chronic stage of leukemia for a long time. The next stage would be the "blast stage," where deformed cells called blasts would start showing up in the bone marrow. When the blasts are discovered, the patient seldom lives longer than a month. The doctor then said cheerfully, "No blasts so far!"

Randy asked the doctor how much longer he really had. The doctor said, "We really can't know at this point. Let's control the white blood cells, work on you being healthy in other ways, and take is as it comes."

"Has anyone ever been cured of leukemia?" Randy asked.

The doctor shook his head and said, "No."

Alone in the darkness, Randy wondered, *"How do you plan for the future when you have no future? When the amount of time you have is so uncertain, do you go to college? And for what purpose? To get a job? Yet, why not skip college and go right for the job?"* Randy hated the thought of having limited time to live and of spending that time just earning money and making no real difference. But he had to eat, and he didn't feel his parents should be supporting him. In Italy where he was teaching people about the gospel, Randy had no doubts about the value of his efforts or whether or not he was doing the right thing. Now, he longed for that clarity.

And Should We Die . . .

Between tests, visitors, and frequent cat naps, Randy read the scriptures, prayed, and wrote his thoughts and ideas on paper. He was not sure what he was going to do with the rest of his short life, but he was going to make sure he did something that mattered.

As time passed, Randy continued to improve and gain weight. After such a long time of worry and uncertainty, Randy's parents were visibly relieved by his progress. Two weeks after being admitted, Randy was doing so well that he was allowed to go home.

An amazing number of postcards and letters were waiting for Randy when he settled into his old bedroom. Postcards from missionaries all over the mission wished him well and reminded him that their prayers were with him. One wrote:

> *"Dear Elder McMillan,*
> *I'm Elder Grant. You may not know me, but I know all about you. I have (had) some good companions in the mission that knew you and grew from their associations with you. I'm sorry I never got to meet the legendary Elder McMillan, because I can see what a big influence you've made on your past associates . . .*
> *Hang in there. You've got a tremendous testimony to bear to a lot of people still . . .*
> *Best wishes.*
> *Elder Grant"*

President Grinceri wrote Randy's parents and thanked them for raising "such a man of faith." He told them that in Italy the average baptism rate is two baptisms per missionary for the full two years. He went on to mention that Randy was the top missionary with 30 baptisms, and he reminded them that Randy had only served 18 months. He also shared with them that several of the people Randy taught while in the hospital had also joined the church.

Randy tearfully gave a letter to his folks from the hospital in Parma. His parents were concerned about the costs of Randy's medical treatment in Italy. Howard's insurance covered him stateside, but there were serious doubts about whether or not his insurance would cover the bills from Italy. Howard joked that if they came to foreclose on Randy, he'd "have to let the Italians have him." The letter from the hospital, written in English, was addressed to Randy's parents. It expressed condolences for Randy's condition and wished him and his parents the best. It also stated that it had been a privilege to be of help to someone of their son's caliber and that the hospital was pleased to dismiss all charges. An accompanying note, in Italian, shared the doctor's fondness for Randy and thanked him for the cheer he brought to their work. All the doctors had refused payment for their services. They wished Randy and his family the best of memories together.

On Sunday, Randy attended stake conference with over 600 people in attendance. The visiting general authority invited Randy to come to the pulpit and speak. Randy humbly expressed his gratitude for the love and compassion that everyone had shown him and his family. He talked about his illness in Italy and the shock of learning about his leukemia. He closed by expressing his gratitude to the Lord for this trial and hoped the Lord would use it to accomplish good. "I trust the Lord," he said, and he honestly meant it.

The day after stake conference, Randy received a call from a reporter at the Ogden Standard Examiner. She had heard about

Randy's situation and thought it would make a good human interest story. She asked if he would let her interview him for the paper. "Sure," Randy said, and they set an appointment.

The reporter came to Randy's home. She met some of the family, then was left alone with Randy in the living room.

Her first question surprised Randy and his reply surprised her.

"So, Elder McMillan,"

"Please call me Randy."

"Okay. So Randy, what does it feel like to know you are going to die?"

Randy paused just a beat and responded, "Great! It feels great to know I'm going to die."

The reporter looked puzzled. "What do you mean it feels great to know you're going to die?"

"When are you going to die?" Randy pressed.

"I don't know."

"That's right. You don't know. You might die when you're eighty-five or maybe you'll be hit by a garbage truck and die tomorrow. Right?"

"I suppose so."

"So, I'm willing to bet that because you don't know when you are going to die, you assume you have a long time and have given little thought to preparing yourself to go. Am I right?"

"Yes. That's true," she admitted.

"Well," Randy said, getting animated, "I know I'm going to die soon. So, because my time is limited, I want every day to count. I want to live so as to be ready to die any day. I focus on what matters, and I feel great as a result."

At that point, she seemed to drop out of her role as reporter asking, "So what matters, Randy?"

In the Long Silence of the Night

"I believe that when we are in the service to our fellow man, we are only in the service of our God."

She nodded thoughtfully, not aware that Randy was paraphrasing Mormon scripture.

Randy continued, "And I believe the glory of God is intelligence, so to partake of that glory, we have to learn, acquire knowledge, and grow."

She started making notes in her pad.

"And, I believe man is that he might have joy and that he might have it more abundantly." She nodded and seemed to be seriously considering each statement.

"Therefore, what matters?" Randy held up his fingers. "First, service to God and our fellow men. Second, learning and growing. And third, experiencing joy in my journey. And that's what I'm doing. That's why I feel great."

Randy did not intend to pass off the doctrines he was espousing as his own. Of course, he was Mormon and he believed what the Church taught. However, the reporter, not being familiar with Mormon doctrine and not having Randy help her with sources, assumed that Randy was a young, rather brilliant philosopher. The interview lasted about an hour and a half.

The article was printed the following week. The title in big black lettering said: AGAIN CLEARFIELD LDS MISSIONARY BATTLES FOR LIFE. The quarter page article included a large picture of Randy reading a book. The caption read: "Mormon Church missionary Randy McMillan, a leukemia victim, studies scriptures at his Clearfield home." The article mentioned Randy surviving the trench cave-in, and it talked about his Italian mission and being called home early due to his sickness. It omitted most of

Randy's thoughts on life but was interesting and complimentary. Though published in the Ogden Standard Examiner, it was picked up by the UPI and appeared in newspapers all over the West.

Randy began receiving phone calls from around the intermountain region asking him to come speak to a wide variety of groups: church groups, school groups, sororities, business groups, community groups. People had read the article, called telephone information, and asked for the only McMillans in Clearfield.

The first invitation came from a school in Ogden.

"Hello, this is Randy."

"Hi, Randy. You don't know me. I'm the principal of St. Joseph's Catholic school in Ogden. I read the article about you in the newspaper and I was wondering if you could come and talk to my students."

"I would be happy to. What would you like me to talk to them about?" Randy asked.

"Your experience with a terminal illness; how you've dealt with it, your perspective on life, your testimony."

"Yes, I would be happy to. Are you aware that I'm LDS?"

"Yes."

"Well, I mention it because my perspective and testimony are based on my religious beliefs," Randy said cautiously.

"Oh, that makes no difference. What I want is someone with a positive outlook on life that can encourage my kids to believe and not get discouraged," the priest said hopefully.

Randy showed up at the agreed upon time and was surprised that he was to be the speaker for a student body assembly. He had expected to talk with 20 kids in a classroom—not all the students in the school.

Randy spoke about growing up in Clearfield and had them laughing about some of his dating experiences. He shared with them the shock of finding out he had a fatal illness. He shared with them that one of the most important things they could do in life would be to serve others. He told them that whenever they felt down and discouraged, they should look around to see who was in need; then, they should reach out and help them. He stated that serving others fills a person with the light of Christ and chases out discouragement. He strongly advocated that it's not what happens to you in life that matters, it's what you do about what happens to you that matters. He said, "That's what will make you into the person God wants you to be." He closed by telling them how precious and wonderful life is, and he pleaded with them to not waste a day of it and challenged them to live a life that matters.

Afterwards, even though the bell had rung, a long line of students formed to talk to him and thank him. The principal thanked him over and over again for the gift Randy had given his school.

The next two weeks were spent getting tests and treatment in the hospital, then mostly laying around home resting up.

Randy was asked to meet with the Church missionary committee. He dressed in a suit and went with his parents to Salt Lake City. The members of the committee talked with Randy about his medical condition and his feelings about his mission and his illness. They decided to give Randy an honorable release from his mission, which meant that Randy would not be returning to serve the final six months of his two-year call. Anticipating their decision, Randy was not particularly disappointed, but he was humbled with how this small group of people with responsibility for over 20,000 full-time missionaries throughout the world gave him such care and personal attention.

Randy's 84-year-old grandmother, Mary, had moved in with his parents while he was on his mission. He loved having the time to talk with her and learn more about her life.

And Should We Die . . .

Listening to Grandma Mary's stories inspired Randy. He began reading some of the old journals and books about his ancestors.

On his mother's side, Randy came through the Richardsons. In 1850 Edmund, his wife, and two children were on the Oregon Trail, hoping to settle in Oregon. The Richardson's wagon broke down near Fort Bridger, Wyoming. The wagon train leaders, fearing the mountain snows of the late summer if they delayed, expressed their regrets and abandoned the little family to the Indians, the elements, and the Mormons.

The Richardsons decided to winter in the Salt Lake Valley, close enough to the Mormon settlement to be safe from the Indians and close enough to the Indians to be safe from the Mormons. They were befriended by the Mormon settlers, and after a thorough examination of their religion, "coupled with a prayerful search," they joined the Church of Jesus Christ of Latter-day Saints.

Randy read about Edmund and Mary settling Manti, Utah. Mary gave birth to two boys and adopted an orphan Indian girl. Both Edmund and Mary eventually succumbed to sickness, and their deaths made orphans of the five children. Randy's great-grandfather, Charles Edmund, age 13, took his 11-year-old brother and joined up with a wagon train going to Arizona. Later, they moved to the Mormon colonies in Mexico. Randy read, wide-eyed, of their encounters with Poncho Villa and Geronimo. Geronimo hated the Mericats (Americans) and the Mexicanos, but he lived in peace with the Mormones (Mormons).

Randy's grandfather, Mark, was born in Colonia Diaz, then moved to Snowflake, Arizona. He married Mary Lundquist and finally settled in Salt Lake City, where Beverly was born.

Through the McMillan side, Randy was also a fifth-generation Mormon. His great-great grandfather, Daniel McMillan, was born in

In the Long Silence of the Night

Dumbarton, Scotland, and converted to the Church of Jesus Christ of Latter-day Saints in Liverpool, England, in 1840 along with his friends and son Ephriam. Daniel immigrated with his family, crossed the plains and settled in Heber, Utah, in 1865. Because of their poverty, Ephriam came later, working his way across the Atlantic as a sailor, then by train to the Missouri River. He then drove six yoke of oxen, trailing two wagons, on the thousand-mile journey to Utah. The oxen were not tame and had to be tied each morning in order to fasten the yoke. They were actually herded across the plains instead of driven. During an unusually early blizzard, Ephriam went in search of strays and was lost in the storm. When found, he was unconscious and nearly frozen to death. It took him a full year to recover from his frostbite. Ephriam married Mary Day (who had immigrated from England) and become a printer for the Deseret News, then for a small newspaper in Heber. Randy's grandfather, also named Ephriam, married Janette Gibson and became a hard rock miner in Park City, where Howard was born and raised.

Randy read of sacrifice and service and felt that his legacy from these brave pioneers should be earned. Reading these family journals and books gave him an intense interest in tracing his family lines and discovering more about his "roots." On days when he felt strong, he drove his dad's Chevy to the genealogical library in Salt Lake City. A helpful researcher told him this was the largest collection of genealogical references and records in the world and showed Randy how to research names, birth dates, birth places, marriages, and death dates. Randy was hooked. He began extracting family group sheets for his personal Book of Remembrance. Family members cheered him on, and extended family offered helpful information and records. Randy felt that his efforts were part of fulfilling the word of scripture in that his work helped to turn the hearts of the fathers to the children and the hearts of the children to the fathers.

Randy's hobby turned into a vocation when he discovered that a small company named "The Ancestral Research Center" was hiring genealogical researchers and that they had a special need for researchers who could read Italian records. Randy applied and was hired.

Randy was also called to be a ward mission leader and stake missionary. This calling gave him responsibilities for missionary work in the area where he lived, but only a part-time effort was expected. His area included Hill Air Force Base. And unlike full time missionaries, a lot of the strict rules did not apply; he could even date and party late!

As winter became spring, the doctors informed Randy that his leukemia was officially "in remission." His blood cell count was normal. For all intents and purposes he was back to normal; however, they warned him that at any time, without warning, the leukemia could attack, so vigilance and constant monitoring was still needed.

By May of 1977, Randy had a paying job he loved, he was doing missionary work and teaching people about the gospel, he was giving about two speeches and firesides a month to very interested audiences, and he was physically feeling great with the leukemia in complete remission. Against his mother's wishes, he even bought a Kawasaki 500 motorcycle. And knowing what it was like to be without these blessings, Randy was grateful for every single one of them.

Randy had no way of knowing that everything he had ever learned about faith, prayer, and dealing with adversity was about to be pushed to the most extreme limits.

Chapter 8

Red Castle

Still sitting on the living room floor, I picked up a photo of Randy, Blake and someone I didn't recognize bunched together on a pile of rocks.

"Where was this taken?" I asked.

"Mount Wilson."

"I didn't realize you made it all the way to the summit."

"Just barely," Randy sighed, looking at the picture.

"Randy, I never really got the whole story. Blake doesn't like to talk about it, so I've never really pressed him to learn what happened."

"I guess I've avoided the subject too. I feel so bad about what happened. It was awful and it was wonderful, but I never should have put Blake through it. I made a big mistake."

"So," I asked, slipping into my interviewer role, "what does Red Castle mean to you now?"

Randy was thoughtful for a moment.

"Red Castle is a battle fought and a battle won."

And Should We Die . . .

Randy loved riding his motorcycle fast. He loved the feeling of being free, the feeling of flying, the feeling of being alive. He began commuting the 30 miles to work everyday on his Kawasaki 500.

Riding home on a sizzling summer day, he was heading north on Beck Street, leaving Salt Lake. The two cars in front of him pulled off, leaving him behind an old, stinky, smokey tanker truck. The other lane was full, and he could see no way around the truck until it reached the freeway. Randy's bike hit a deep pothole, then another, and the 400 advertizing flyers he had strapped to his sissy bar scattered all over the highway. Randy pulled to the side, set his bike on the kickstand, and began chasing the flyers fluttering in the gust of each passing car. After collecting about 300, he gave up on the rest. Four lanes of traffic with cars traveling at 45 miles an hour proved to be too much of a challenge.

He heard sirens approaching—not one, but five or six. He saw the flashing lights of police cars and fire engines. "My heavens," he thought "this is a bit of an overreaction to some unintentional littering."

The emergency vehicles raced past, and Randy saw a black towering cloud of smoke ahead. Picking up flyers, he had not noticed the spreading blackness. Traffic came to a halt and started backing up.

Randy strapped the recovered flyers securely to the back of his bike and took advantage of his mode of transportation by weaving in between the waiting cars and traveling down the striped lines delineating the traffic lanes.

There was a violent fire about a half-mile down the road. The tanker Randy had been riding behind had been in some sort of an accident, and oil and fire were covering both sides of the highway. Randy hoped no one was hurt. The fire engines were spraying water in an attempt to slow the spreading flames. He eased his bike off the road, beyond the stopped cars, through some weeds and gravel, and onto a side road, effectively bypassing the dangerous scene.

Riding home, Randy wondered, *"What would have happened if the flyers had not come loose? Would I have been riding behind the tanker when it exploded?"* It seemed to him that the flyers coming loose when they did saved him from serious harm, maybe even death. Images flooded his mind: the pig man in his blood-covered apron; the suffocating trench; the frightened, dying driver in the desert; a black night in his Italian hospital room. Had his death been delayed again? Why? Was the fluttering of the flyers the Lord's protection or just a coincidence? If Heavenly Father had protected him and spared him from death, for what reason? For what purpose? Randy wondered what his future would hold, and how he could know it. With his leukemia in remission, he might have years, instead of months, to live. Should he consider college? Marriage and a family? In some ways it seemed easier to live expecting imminent death—you just set your mind to holding on and enduring. But when you have two years or maybe even five, it was difficult to plan. These thoughts occupied Randy on the long road home and late into the night.

With each passing day, Randy felt better and stronger. He began playing handball and basketball, and resumed weight-lifting and jogging. He gained muscle weight and added some lost definition.

Randy began plotting against his mother's wishes. Every year for nine years, until he left on his mission, Randy had gone backpacking into the primitive area of Utah's Uinta mountains to an incredible place called Red Castle. Depending on which peaks they summited, it was a 30-mile round-trip hike with full backpacks. Randy was feeling strong enough to make the trip. His mom felt he would be taking an awful chance. Blake was willing to go, but Danny and Ron had to work and Melba was taking care of her new baby. Howard felt Randy was a big boy and ought to decide for himself. So he did and scheduled the hike for late August. He also arranged with the research center for a week off work.

The pick-up truck slid to a stop, and the trailing cloud of dust caught up with and completely enveloped them. Randy had driven on the dirt road too fast, but like a kid on Christmas morning, he did not want to wait even an extra minute to start their adventure. They waited for the dust to settle somewhat and climbed out of the cab. Parked against the trees were several horse trailers. *"Lousy luck ,"* thought Randy. *"I hope we don't have to dodge horse piles all the way to the castle."* Randy, along with his 15-year-old brother Blake, and a friend, William, shouldered their 60-pound backpacks, locked the truck, and walked to the trail head. Randy inhaled the strong scent of pine.

"Well brothers, we're off!" he said, then added back over his shoulder as he started walking, "Don't try to keep up. It will just wear you down, and I don't want to have to carry either of you old men out."

The trail wove through a small grove then broke into the open. A wide, ice-clear stream about thigh deep gently flowed through deep brush and thick, long, avocado-green grass. Here, the canyon floor was wide and spongy, wet with lush vegetation, no trees. Bordering the meadow were steep ridges thickly covered with verdant, dark-green lodge pole pine. And arching from ridge to ridge was a wonderful sky—the high-mountain, brilliant-blue sky. Randy thrilled at the sight—a familiar, cherished friend. Randy was only

Red Castle

11 when Ron first brought him to Red Castle, and ever since it had almost been a pilgrimage, a ritual to return each summer.

The trio followed the well-worn trail for five miles, then took a break. They shed their packs, satisfied their thirst, bit off some buffalo jerky, and sat on a shady log. Randy felt good; he felt strong. Blake, a gifted athlete, was sweating and exuberant. William was struggling. Having recently moved to Utah from Hawaii, the elevation was causing him to feel winded and somewhat faint. They took a long rest.

Eight miles in, the gentle slope of the valley was blocked by a steep shelf and the sleepy stream became a frothy cascade. Instead of slowing, Randy increased his pace to nearly a trot. Up the trail's many switchbacks, through the trees, over a rise—there it stood. Red Castle, a majestic fortress of rocks and crags, pinnacles and buttresses. Every time Randy saw it, he marveled at its grandeur. From its pyramid peak down to its square sides, the rocks had a pinkish hue, which made them stand out from the surrounding gray granite peaks and form a striking contrast with the dark green pines and royal blue sky. At the end of the canyon, the side ridges closed together—like the top of a valentine heart—with Red Castle placed at the point, lording over the whole valley.

A mile further in, the hikers reached Red Castle Lake, a large shiny surface, mirroring the castle and magnifying its size. Ahead to the right, and massive rock wall closed the canyon and atop lay Middle Lake. Above the tree line, in the bowl formed by the curving ridge, lay Upper Lake.

Randy scanned the wall. Though the last of the winter snow had melted a few weeks ago, the waterfall emptying Middle Lake still flowed. With great drama and outstretched arms, Randy turned to his companions and announced, "Welcome to heaven!"

And Should We Die . . .

They set up camp in some old growth pines, gathered firewood, then perched on large boulders by the stream. Like excited children waiting for fireworks to begin, they chattered and speculated on what the sunset would bring. As the sun slipped behind the western ridge, its shadow crept closer, covered them and the lake, and then assaulted the castle. Mount Wilson turned gold, and the castle looked orange. Then, almost in an instant, it turned red—glowing red—the red of embers after the yellow flame is spent. The trio kept a reverential silence. The shadow climbed the mighty rock, reached the final height, then the entire terrestrial realm was dark.

The campers built a fire and warmed some beef stew, sopped it up with sour dough rolls, and washed it down with icy water from the stream.

Before turning in, they put on their heavy coats and left the warmth of the fire. They passed through the trees to the edge of the meadow and looked at the sky. Up this high, with the atmosphere so thin and being over 50 miles from the nearest city lights, the stars were amazing—huge, bright orbs that seemed almost close enough to touch. The Milky Way had multiplied a hundred times since last seen in the Salt Lake Valley, and the Pleiades were truly seven sisters, not a faint vague clump. The air quickly cooled. The campers reluctantly wiggled into their bags, and as they drifted off, Randy's heart was filled with gratitude.

The next morning while the castle was still a black silhouette, the adventurers cooked up oatmeal and scrambled eggs for breakfast; they wanted to get an early start. Their objective was to summit the 13,000 foot Mt. Wilson. Having done it before, Randy confidently planned to make it to the top and return to Middle Lake by three o'clock, then fish until dusk and have fresh rainbow trout for dinner. William noticed they hadn't bought any rods or gear. "How are you going to fish?" he asked. Randy explained how at the top of the waterfall, Middle Lake empties through narrow rock fissures and cracks. Crawling on their bellies, they sneak up to the cracks and look for fish. When they spot one, they slip their hand into the water, careful to make no ripples, then approaching the fish from behind, they strike, hooking the fish through the gills with their fingers, or failing that, trapping them against the rock side with their palm and pulling them out. "We get our limit every time," Randy bragged.

"Is that legal?" William quizzed.

"Only in primitive wilderness areas when the game wardens aren't around," Randy smugly answered.

Sidewalking ledges and bouldering refrigerator-sized rocks, they climbed the wall. They hiked around the west side of the lake, angling up the ridge toward Porcupine Pass. Randy slowed. Something was wrong. He asked for frequent rests. His head started pounding.

"What's wrong?" Blake asked. He was worried.

"I don't know. Out of shape, I guess."

William started complaining of dizziness. Randy took longer rests, but they failed to renew his strength. He ate an energy bar and drank his whole canteen but still had no energy. However, William started feeling a bit better.

They reached Porcupine Pass and had an incredible view. To the south they could see the vast forest spotted with lakes and on the far horizon, the Manti-Lasal Mountain Range. To the north they could see the route they took to get here, and beyond, the badlands of Wyoming. Randy found a flat rock to lay on and slept for half an hour.

Blake woke him. "Let's call this our summit," Blake suggested, "and head back to camp."

Randy shook his head. "I'm going to the top."

"I don't think that's such a good idea. You're not lookin' so good. Let's get you down to camp and rest you up."

"Go back if you want. I'm going to the top." Randy knew he was being stubborn. He knew he was pursuing a dangerous course, but he was determined to climb another half mile in distance and another thousand vertical feet. He was angry that his body was trying to limit him, slow him, stop him. He also knew that this problem was much more than being out of shape. He recognized the symptoms—his leukemia was back. "*Well, in your face!*" he told himself. He was angry. In his mind, he cursed the disease. "*You are the enemy! And you will not defeat me!*" He stood and began climbing on his own. Blake let out a loud breath and reluctantly followed.

Near the top, Randy took three steps then rested, three steps then rested. He eventually stood on the top of the narrow, rounded peak, breathing hard. The threesome posed while the camera's self-timer ticked down. The photo taken, Randy walked 20 yards back down the mountain to a flat rock and took an hour nap.

To the west, Blake could see Haden Peak and Bald Mountain. Mount Timpanogos, of the Wasatch Mountains, formed the distant skyline 70 miles away. To the east he could see the 14,000 foot King's Peak and the other major peaks of the Uintas' spine. This truly seemed to be the top of the world.

Blake walked down to his brother. Randy was pale, and he was sucking in big breaths through his nose and letting them out slowly through his mouth (an old wrestling trick to prevent hyperventilating). He was not getting enough oxygen.

"Lets get goin'," Blake urged.

Randy sat up, then stood up and started walking down the mountain. They went slowly, with Randy resting. The descent was definitely easier than the assent, but taxing nevertheless.

They reached Middle Lake at sunset, climbed down the wall and stumbled into camp in the dark. Randy made himself eat, then crashed into his bed.

Come morning, Randy did not feel rested. He was extremely fatigued and in pain. The trio never discussed whether or not to cut their trip short. Blake and William broke camp and lightened Randy's pack by three fourths. They helped him slip the pack on and started walking slowly down the trail toward the truck. Even with less weight and frequent rests, Randy collapsed before they had gone halfway. He could not walk anymore. William started feeling nauseous and light headed. He had mountain sickness, brought on by the altitude, and it was getting worse.

Blake knew the seriousness of the situation. Without a transfusion and medical attention, Randy would most likely die.

William was useless because of his sickness, and if his situation worsened he would be in real danger. Blake set up camp for Randy and William. He filled their canteens and laid out everything that was edible but required no cooking. At his insistence, Blake helped Randy to his knees. Together, the three knelt and said a heart-felt prayer, asking for the Lord's blessings upon them. Blake left his pack and started hiking, hoping to locate some horses that could be brought back to carry Randy and William out. He ran down the rough trail, praying he could complete his task in time to save Randy's life.

After covering what he guessed to be five miles, Blake broke through a cluster of trees. About two miles ahead, on the other side of the meadow, he spotted some men on horseback riding away toward the trail head. Blake increased his pace, pushing past his limits. The sun was setting as Blake stumbled into the parking area, exhausted. The horse trailers were gone. Looking down the road, he could see the dust of a recently departing vehicle. He ran up the knoll just in time to see the horse trailer disappear down the road. Blake jumped and shouted and waved his arms, but the trailer, truck, and the precious horses were gone.

Blake assessed his situation: it was getting dark and cold, he was without a coat or a sleeping bag, he had neither a flashlight nor the means of making a fire, and he did not have any food. In his haste, he had not even thought to bring the keys to the truck. To try and follow the trail back to Randy and William in the night would be impossible and dangerous. His brother was dying and Blake was alone. He walked to their truck, opened the cab, and sat inside. Simply and humbly he prayed for help and comfort for himself, William, and Randy.

Though the ground and forest were black, the sky was still light when Blake heard a distant motor. A car was coming. He stepped out of the truck and watched a small Toyota Sedan pull to a stop in the clearing. Out climbed a middle-aged man and two large German shepherds. The man pulled a backpack from the trunk while the two dogs sniffled toward Blake. The man called them and they quickly returned to him. He commanded them to stay (which they did), then walked over to Blake. He asked a few questions, and discovering Blake's predicament, offered help. He dug an extra sleeping bag out of his car and gave Blake some trail mix and beef jerky. He said he wished he could do more to help, but he had some important things to attend to. Then, he and the dogs took off into the night.

Blake climbed back into the bag and sat upright in the truck's cab. He wolfed down the trail mix. He saw the first stars of the night and then noticed some movement near the trail head. The figure drew closer, and when it reached the truck, Blake recognized William.

"What are you doing here?" Blake asked.

"I started feeling better, so Randy told me to go find you. The last mile was totally dark. I fell several times and hurt my ankle pretty bad. Any luck with the horses?" William wondered.

"No. I just missed them. So Randy is out there all alone?" Blake asked the obvious.

William nodded.

"What are we going to do?"

William replied, "Without a flashlight, not much we can do until morning."

They unpacked William's backpack and set up his tent next to the truck. William gave Blake an extra sweatshirt. Blake pulled it on and climbed into his newly acquired sleeping bag. He laid on the seat.

He felt upset that William had abandoned Randy on the trail. Why had Randy sent him away? Was he worried about his little brother? Did he realize getting the horses was a long shot? Did he want to die by himself? "Oh God," Blake prayed, "don't let Randy die out there in the darkness—all alone."

Blake turned on the radio. Clear and strong he heard the Mormon Tabernacle Choir. It was a rebroadcast of "The Music and the Spoken Word" from Temple Square. As he listened to the beautiful singing, he felt a sweet calm come over him. His worry left; his fear left. He felt so peaceful and serene. Something deep inside assured him that all was well. He turned off the radio and relaxed into an undisturbed sleep.

When Blake awoke, the Eastern sky was glowing. It was an hour before sunrise. He opened the truck door and was assaulted by the cold. Had it snowed? He pulled off the sleeping bag, forced on his stiff boots, and stepped outside. A thick hoarfrost covered the ground and trees, and in the ripening morning the world glowed white. He wanted to crawl back into his bag for protection from the cold, but he thought of Randy. Blake started running up the trail, slipping and stumbling on the slick, frosty rocks.

As Blake ran, he warmed up, expelling white puffs with every breath. The rising sun illuminated the white pines on the far ridge, making them all crystalline and sparkles. Instead of wondrous, to Blake it looked hard and cold.

Nearing Randy's camp, Blake slowed. Breathing hard, he leaned against a tree. He was not sure what the next few steps would reveal, not sure he wanted to see.

He saw Randy's tent, then his frost-covered sleeping bag outside the tent. Why wasn't it inside? Drawing closer he could see Randy's head half-out the bag. It was covered with icy white. Blake froze. The bag did not move. Randy's head did not move.

Blake hesitated a moment longer, then slowly approached. He bent down and touched Randy's neck. Warm. Randy stirred. Opening his eyes, he whispered, "Hey Bro."

"How are you feeling?" Blake asked.

"Not so good."

Blake softly brushed Randy's head with his fingers. "Your hair is frozen. Don't you have enough sense to get in out of the cold?"

Randy mumbled, "I wanted to see the stars."

Blake sat Randy up, still in his bag. "What are we going to do?"

It took a moment to get his mind functioning. Then Randy said, "Let's get out of here."

Red Castle

He slowly put on his boots and his coat, then sat on a stump and directed Blake to pack up the camp, burn all the food in the fire pit, lash the two packs together, and put them on. Blake struggled under the weight.

Randy seemed totally focused on the task at hand, resolved to see it through.

"Are you going to be able to walk out?" Blake questioned.

Randy ignored Blake's question and started down the trail with a steady gait. Blake followed, looking much like an ant carrying an impossibly large boulder on its back.

Several minutes later, Blake was out of breath.

"Randy . . . got to rest . . . for a minute." Blake shed his burden, sat on the wet grass, and leaned against a tree. He slowly sucked in deep breaths while Randy seemed to walk in place or pace in small circles. It was as if Randy feared that if he stopped he would not be able to get going again. Randy walked to Blake and grabbed the pack. "Let's get going." He tried to lift it to help Blake on with it, but he did not have enough strength.

Blake hefted the weight against the tree, then while pressing it did a turn, holding the pack up with his back. He slipped his arms through the harness, took a few steps, and started walking.

Randy was exhausted. He shuffled and tripped several times on roots or rocks his feet did not quite clear. It was afternoon when the tortured pair reached the truck. William was weak and dizzy again and laying in the cab.

"You okay?" William asked Randy.

Randy gave a shrug with his shoulders as if to say "still alive," and with William's help he got seated in the truck. Blake threw the gear in the back, rolled up the borrowed sleeping bag, and placed it on the top of the Toyota. He wrote, "Thanks!" on the dust of the hood.

And Should We Die . . .

"Do you feel up to driving us out of here?" Blake asked William. "Because I don't know how to drive."

William said simply, "I can drive," and took the keys.

Randy slumped against the door and did not speak or stir during the three-hour drive home.

Chapter 9

Yet Another Miracle

We sat in a nice room at the University of Utah Medical Center. Randy was sitting up in the hospital bed with tight rolls of cotton, white and red, sticking out of his nose. The doctors had just cauterized his nasal passages to stop the bleeding. This time, Randy had bled for 15 hours, a heavy flow which they could not get stopped. His heart was beating way too fast, his blood pressure was way too low, and when they were examining him, he had passed out. Everyone had been hoping this procedure would stop the bleeding.

"Are you sure you want to do this now?" I wondered. "Work on the book?"

"Yeah, might as well. Nothing else to do." He seemed to be feeling okay.

"That must have been an awful night up at Red Castle, all alone."

Randy nodded and was thoughtful for a moment. "Yeah, it was. While I was lying in the tent, I started feeling claustrophobic. I tried to sleep, but I would float in and out, not really asleep, but not quite awake. You know?"

"Yeah, I know what that's like. It's hell," I said, speaking from experience.

"I kept hearing sounds," Randy continued. "So I'd think the horses had come to haul me out. I'd get up on my elbow and unzip the tent, flash the trail with my light, and nobody was there. I swear, one time I heard a truck all rattling and clanking; then I got a shiver—it was the pig man! The pig man was coming to get me!"

"The pig man?" I asked.

"Yeah."

"From Fiddler's Creek? The guy who butchered our beef?" I was amazed.

"Yeah. Remembering it now, it sounds crazy. But up there I thought it was real. And I kept getting a shovel and crawling down into the trench."

"The cave-in? When you were buried alive?"

"Yeah, and I saw blood on my hands from the crash in Southern Utah."

"Oh, Randy . . . "

"Finally, I crawled out of the tent and pulled my bag out. The camp fire had died down. It was coal-black and cold. The pain in my gut made it hard to move. It hurt so bad. I got in my bag and reached to zip it up. I guess I closed my eyes—because of the pain—and I think I passed out, or maybe almost did. But the next thing I knew, I opened my eyes, and there were those huge, magnificent stars. So beautiful, so bright. I was so close to them they didn't even twinkle, just had a steady white glow."

Randy's eyes filled with tears; his voice trembled with emotion. "It was so beautiful. I just gazed at this marvelous sight and said a prayer. 'My Father, I thank thee . . . for so much . . . for everything. I want to

Yet Another Miracle

live. Please let me live. But nevertheless, thy will be done. I submit to thee.'" He paused, reflecting. Then he looked up and said adamantly, "And Ron, I meant it. I really meant it. If he wanted me to die, then I would, right there. But I sure wanted to live."

The two of us were quiet. Randy wiped his eyes with his sleeve.

"What's the deal with Blake?" I said, lightening the mood. "He's not a pack horse, you know."

Randy smiled, "Blake was amazing. He's a real hero."

"He sure grew up on that trip," I reported.

"I don't know what I was thinking. I should have left all that camp gear there with a note saying 'You're welcome to it.' But I knew what I had to do to get out: stand up, start walking, and not stop no matter what. Blake was a trooper. I don't know how he did it."

"He feels that he was helped along by an angel or unseen force," I said.

"I'm sure he was; we both were," Randy nodded thoughtfully.

"So, what happened when you got out of the mountains and the doctor got hold of you?"

"He ordered all the tests. I felt like a human pin cushion."

"And what did they find?" I was taking notes.

"My white blood cell count was 250,000."

"You went from normal to 250,000 in three weeks?"

"Apparently. But that's not all. This time they found deformed white blood cells. My leukemia had reached the blast crisis. They also found abnormal cells in my spinal fluid."

"What did the doctor say?"

"He was very caring, almost apologetic. He told me that the chances of me living more than a month were very slim."

"What was your reaction?"

"I gave him a hug and thanked him for getting me this far on my journey."

And Should We Die . . .

Randy pondered long into the night. His doctor had told him that there were deformed cells in the spinal fluid. The doctor was not aware of a single case where a patient had lived longer than a month once this progression of the disease had occurred, and they ordered an aggressive regimen of chemotherapy administered orally, through IVs, and through painful spinal taps. They would use frequent transfusions. They would use steroids. They would use painkillers. They would fight hard as long as they could. While there were no medications that would help, Randy concluded that he had finally been given a time frame. He no longer had to wonder; he had one month, probably less, to live.

When he had first returned from Italy, Randy figured he had some time, though not a lot. He had settled into life, savoring his experiences, trying to fight the good fight. But something had happened when the leukemia had gone into remission. He felt good. It was not until he felt healthy that he realized how awful his suffering had been. He relished being pain-free and active. Randy had started to expect that he would live. Without really thinking it through, he had felt that maybe he had beat his own death sentence. Now, he realized it was not to be. His hopes had been false hopes. He dreaded the slide into intensifying pain, the debilitating weakness, the fatigue, the immobility, the fuzzy stupor. He was familiar with all of these enemies, and now they would lay siege and, he was certain, conquer in the end.

Over the next several days, Randy slid into a deep depression. The fight was over, he told himself. Let the inevitable happen. He closed off family and friends, not wanting to "entertain" visitors or talk with anyone. He called his coworkers at the research center and explained the situation. They told him to work at getting better, and they would hold his job for him.

Randy's mother insisted that he come home where she could take care of him. They moved Randy out of the hospital against the medical staff's better judgement.

At home, Randy picked at his food, watched TV, and wanted to be alone. He was grumpy and irritable. The problem, from his point of view, was that his family would not leave him alone. Mom and Dad insisted on telling him the news of the day and sitting with him while he watched television. Several friends a day dropped by to express concern and chat about their current problems or adventures. They would not leave him alone either and kept pulling him into life.

Then the letters started arriving; everyday more letters. Some came from missionaries, catching him up on the latest and encouraging him to have faith. Some were from high school students he had talked with, expressing thanks for his message. Some letters were from parents, thanking him for the influence his ideas had on their children. One was from a sociology professor at the University of Utah who described the positive difference Randy's comments had made in his students' education. Three or four of the letters were from people dying of terminal illnesses. They wrote about the challenge Randy had given them to discover the meaning of their suffering and lose themselves in service to others. They thanked him for being frank with them and giving them a reason to keep on going. Randy's mother sat next to Randy and read aloud some of the letters; other letters she just placed next to him, and he read them when he felt up to it. The bishop of a local congregation wrote:

And Should We Die . . .

"Dear Elder McMillan,

We would like to try to express to you the gratitude we feel deep in our hearts for the very special testimony you shared with us last Sunday evening . . . Listening to you, and feeling of your complete trust in the Lord, of your strong, positive attitude and the courage you so bravely manifest that gave each of us the desire to improve our lives and to accept your challenge to dedicate our lives to God's service . . . If only those of us in that audience would be as well prepared to meet our Lord and Savior as you are! . . . No one of us will ever be the same again because of you, Randy . . . May God continue to guide you and give you the strength to speak and so profoundly influence those of us (who are in need).

Our sincere love and prayers . . ."

It was signed by the bishop.

Randy was touched by the letters. He was surprised that so many had been affected by his words and that they had been thoughtful enough to write him and express their thanks.

One evening Randy received a phone call from a youth leader in Provo. She had heard about his presentation from another youth leader in Brigham City and wondered if Randy would come talk to 250 teenagers during a weekend event scheduled to happen in 8 weeks. Without thinking, Randy said he would and wrote the information on the family calender. His dad was amused by the proceedings, and after Randy hung up, Howard casually remarked, "Well, it looks like you won't be able to die for another two months."

Randy thought about his dad's comment. It bugged him. Should he not accept any requests to talk? Should he tell people who invited him that he would like to, but he was planning on being dead soon?

Yet Another Miracle

He sat on a reclining lawn chair in the backyard and admired the view of the Wasatch Mountains; the beginning of Fall had speckled the mountainside with red and gold. He took the first letter off of a new pile just retrieved from the mailbox.

The letter was addressed to "Randy McMillen, Clearfield, Utah," with no street address or zipcode. Though his name was misspelled and the address incomplete, the mailman had figured out where in belonged. It was postmarked Las Vegas.

The writer told Randy that although he did not know her, she felt compelled to write to him. She explained that she was an orphan who had been raised by her aunt. She had fallen in love with a boy and had hoped to marry him, but then she found out she was pregnant with his child. Fearful that he would not react well to the news, she procrastinated telling him. The day before she planned to tell him, her boyfriend was killed in an accident. She was shocked by the news and grieved to lose both her lover and the father of her unborn child. She reluctantly told her boyfriend's parents, thinking it was the right thing to do, but they were furious and accused her of trying to tarnish their son's good name. She was devastated. When she told her aunt about her condition, her aunt turned her out, saying she was no longer welcome and this was no longer her home. On her own, pregnant and grieving, she decided to go to Las Vegas, where no one knew her, and end her life.

She hitchhiked as far as Provo, where she called some friends to say goodbye. Not knowing her plans and realizing she was in town, they insisted that she stay the night with them. There was a fireside that evening at their church, and the friends insisted that she come with them. Randy was the speaker. His message deeply moved her. She decided that if Randy could live with his sufferings and still find happiness, so could she. That night she prayed to her Father in

Heaven and asked for his help. She continued to Las Vegas and got a job as a waitress. Learning about her situation, her new boss and his family invited her to live with them until she got on her feet. Her letter explained that she now had a beautiful baby daughter. She had also met and fallen in love with a wonderful man who loved both her and her daughter, and they had plans to marry soon in the St. George temple. She truly was happy.

She ended her letter by saying that she loved Randy in a way no one could ever describe. She thanked Randy for herself and for her daughter and signed it only, "Someone you saved."

Randy carefully folded the letter, held it to his chest, and wept.

Late that night, unable to sleep, Randy dug through his papers. He located and read his patriarchal blessing, stopping to re-read one particular paragraph:

" . . . peace will be yours, wisdom and understanding, and <u>with the accompaniment of the higher Spirit</u> you shall be able to fulfill your righteous desires on earth."

He found Heber Q. Hale's vision of the spirit world that had so touched him while in Italy and read again how Brother Hale learned that some people die because there is important work for them to do on the other side—and that many die because they have not the faith to be healed.

Randy wondered what his blessing meant when it stated that he would be able to fulfill his righteous desires on earth. Which desires were to be fulfilled? Did he have an important work on the other side, and God was calling him home, or did he just lack the faith to be healed? He thought about the dream he'd had when he was young. Had he completed his service, or was he giving up and leaving people who needed him "outside the gate?" He reflected on the many times his life had been spared: the cave-in, the mission President's blessing in Italy, his recovery after getting home and his remission, the truck that exploded and barely missed him, and now he added the Red Castle hike to the list. Surely these were miracles. Truly the Lord had preserved his life, but why? To die now?

He asked himself, *"What are my desires?"* His honest answer was to live and to serve people—to help them, reduce their suffering, give them hope, and point the way to God. Were these righteous desires? All the letters he had been reading gave him confidence that these desires were righteous. He reasoned, *"Well, if these are righteous desires and God has promised me through a patriarch that I will be able to fulfill my righteous desires on earth, then I choose to live. I choose to exercise the faith to be healed. I choose to serve people through sharing my testimony and message. These are my desires and choices, and I have faith they will be fulfilled."*

Randy said a long, heart-felt prayer. He expressed his desires and reminded the Lord of the patriarch's promise. He asked that he be given the opportunity to serve and that his life be extended. He asked that God would protect him from depression and deliver him from leukemia. He then expressed gratitude for the Savior, for his teachings and his atonement, and asked that all these requests be granted him according to his faith in Jesus Christ's power of deliverance. Randy felt a sweet calm—just like the feeling he had experienced while kneeling by his bedside in Italy. He crawled into bed and fell into a delicious, peaceful sleep.

The depression seemed to lift, and over the next few days Randy returned to life. His parents noticed and commented on it. Some of his siblings asked where Mr. Grumps had gone. Though the physical pain got worse, Randy seemed happier, more upbeat.

And Should We Die . . .

Like a spigot suddenly turned on, requests for Randy's firesides and talks increased dramatically. On some weeks he gave up to six presentations. Sometimes, he felt good enough to drive. At other times, his father was his willing chauffeur. He spoke to all kinds of groups. He spoke to a six-person Christian study group at Weber College, then four days later he spoke to over 550 people at a joint stake fireside. He spoke to family groups, church groups, community groups, school groups. He spoke at juvenile detention centers. He began including in his message admonitions about adversity. He told his audiences that trials make us or break us. Our response to trials can make us stronger, more humble, and bring us closer to God, or they can weaken us, embitter us, and alienate us from God. He liked to quote Brigham Young: "The Lord is going to allow us to suffer, but he will make it bearable and productive." Randy spoke of the blessings of adversity and used his life as an example.

Randy had plenty of opportunities to live his message. His response to the weekly chemotherapy was extreme nausea, severe headaches, and absolute exhaustion. He carefully scheduled his treatments around speaking engagements, trying to leave a few days between treatment and presentations so he could rest up.

As October became November, Randy reminded the doctors that though 30 days had passed, he was still around alive and kicking. Some of the nurses began referring to him as their "miracle baby." They were honestly amazed at how he was holding up. His hair was falling out due to the harsh chemicals, but his smile more than compensated for the loss.

Randy woke up early on a cloudy morning in December especially foggy minded. He had suffered an unusually awful response to his last chemo treatment, and for two days he had severe pain and nausea. He realized that he probably should stay in bed, but he resisted because he was close to cracking a tough genealogical problem at the library for a wonderful family and he wanted to see it through.

Several times while dressing, a wave of pain swept over him, causing him to quickly sit before his legs gave way. He put on his parka and cinched the hood, then carefully eased his helmet over his throbbing head. He opened the garage door. It had snowed a few inches during the night, but it was warm. The roads would be ice free though slushy. He stuffed a wipe cloth in his coat pocket to keep his visor clear, straddled his Kawasaki 500, and started the noisy engine. He picked a slow speed suitable to the conditions and began his commute to Salt Lake City.

The pain was horrible. It seemed to be located deep in his abdomen, then spread outward in pulsing bursts through his chest, arms, and legs. The knifing in his head seemed to be from an independent pain—unrelated to the one in his stomach—but lesser only by a few degrees.

As he rode, he noticed a new pain, a different pain, but he couldn't tell where it was coming from. It was a distant pain in the background, but it was steadily working its way to the front. He could not quite locate it. Then he realized it was in his feet. His feet were aching. He glanced down to diagnose the cause. He was perplexed, then shook his head in disbelief. He was so distracted by the pain in his torso that he had forgotten to get fully dressed. He was riding his motorcycle through the splashing slush without socks or shoes. His feet were encased in an icy buildup.

Randy pulled off the freeway in Farmington and sheepishly called his dad. "Could you please come get me. I've got a bit of a problem."

And Should We Die . . .

Randy rode home in the cab of the old Ford, his bike in the back and his feet under the heater.

As a joyous Christmas turned into the new year, 1978, the doctors gave Randy fabulous news. The blasts were gone from his spinal fluid as well as his blood stream. His white blood cell count was normal. His leukemia was miraculously in remission. One older doctor was especially demonstrative.

"I've never, never heard of a leukemia patient in the blast stage going into remission. You are a first! This is amazing!" he shouted, slapping Randy on the back.

Randy rejoiced with them. Then, instead of demanding dinner at an expensive restaurant (one of his favorite ways to celebrate), he began a 24-hour fast to thank God for yet another miracle.

Chapter 10

The Open Road

This was turning into a long session, stretching to three hours. As I caught up with my notes, the pleasant young nurse returned.

"Let's see if we've got this bleeding stopped," she said as she carefully loosened the gauze rolls from each nostril. Then, using little scissor-like thongs, she pulled them out and put them into a plastic bag. The clots, gauze, and fluid made an unsightly mess.

"Sorry," Randy said sheepishly.

"No problem," the nurse responded cheerfully. "I've seen worse." She dabbed at his nose with something that looked like baby wipes. "It's looking good so far. I'll check back in a few minutes and maybe you'll be able to go home." She smiled and left with the bowl and the mess.

Randy shook his head. "You know, I don't mind the male nurses dealing with my messes, but I hate it when Natalie does."

"Maybe it's because you're not trying to get a date with the doctors or male nurses."

He smiled, "She is a foxy lady. Maybe when my hair grows back and my nose quits bleeding, I'll pay her a social visit."

"May I also suggest you wear something other than that hospital gown?" I teased.

"Ya' think? I don't know. I think it shows off some of my better features," he chuckled.

It was good to see him smile. I noticed yet again how warm his smile was.

"Okay, back to work. Where are we?" I re-read some of my notes and made a notation. "Oh, yes, you were feeling good, in remission." I looked up. Randy was holding both hands against his nose and blood was dripping between his fingers.

"Damn." I meant to say it under my breath, but in the small hospital room it sounded more like a shout. I grabbed a towel out of the bathroom, gave it to Randy, and stepped into the hall.

"Can we get some help in here?" I called toward the nurses station. Natalie came at a run.

In minutes, the gauze plugs were back in place, and Randy was cleaned up with a fresh gown. The bed had been changed, and Randy was ready to talk some more. I made some phone calls to change my plans for the afternoon.

"Okay, I'm all yours," I announced.

He smiled. "Sorry to take so much of your day."

"In our busy lives, it's so hard to take the time to just sit and talk. It really is my pleasure, little brother."

He was reassured and I was sincere.

"Now, wasn't it during February when that miracle happened in Idaho?"

"Yes, the end of February." He counted on his fingers. "Only seven months ago."

The Open Road

Randy's health rapidly improved. The headaches disappeared, his strength and energy returned. He started jogging and exercising. He started regaining weight. He treasured his health and loved being active.

Randy got an apartment in Salt Lake—close enough to his work that he could walk to the genealogical library. He relished his independence. He quickly involved himself in a church group of young singles and made many new friendships. Dates, parties, basketball games, church-sponsored service activities, genealogical research, and speaking assignments filled his new cherished life. He could not fit enough into a day.

Randy's radio alarm announced the day's start. He shuffled into the bathroom and as he looked in the mirror, a small stranger looked back. Randy was startled and confused. The left side of his face was paralyzed. Randy called the doctor's office but could not make himself understood. His tongue was thick and uncooperative. Giving up, he quickly dressed and rode his motorcycle to the hospital and waited to see a doctor.

The doctor examined him and concluded that Randy had a case of Bell's Palsy, a painless yet inconvenient malady that causes temporary paralysis. He explained that although doctors didn't know its cause or treatment, it usually went away on its own after several weeks or sometimes, months. He prescribed an eye patch and eye drops to make sure Randy's eye did not dry out.

Randy struggled with his new look. He felt he looked hideous; the drooping side of his face gave him a very strange appearance. When he drank, the liquid would dribble down his face and neck because he could not move the muscles that closed his mouth. He had to frequently use a handkerchief to keep from drooling. He thought his sparse hair looked bad enough, but the eye patch looked worse. The most difficult part of the whole condition was his speech—he could not be understood. The left half of his tongue would not function. Randy labored with the problem. He practiced moving his tongue in different ways to get out a semblance of coherent language.

Randy was scheduled to give a fireside just four days after the onset of Bell's Palsy to a group of several hundred teenagers in Idaho Falls, Idaho. He at first assumed he would have to cancel. But feeling more and more that this was work the Lord wanted him to do, he prayed about it. Randy received a strong feeling that it was important to speak to these kids. He fasted for 24 hours and prayed for help.

The following Sunday night in Idaho Falls, Randy stood at the pulpit in front of over 300 teens and their leaders. Every eye was on him; his appearance created a lot of interest. He began speaking very slowly, slurring his words, yet careful listeners could understand him. He apologized for being difficult to understand and told them about his Bell's Palsy, explaining that "It doesn't hurt." He asked that all in attendance say a prayer in their heart to assist him in sharing his testimony.

Laboriously, Randy described his experience on his mission, being sick, going to the hospital and learning that he was going to die. As he spoke, his voice became stronger, the pace of his speech increased, his words became clear and easily understood, his facial expressions returned to normal. His message seemed especially powerful. He testified of Jesus Christ, of God's love for us, and that trials and suffering are not evidence of his abandonment; rather, trials are steps into his presence. Every symptom of his palsy disappeared. People whispered to each other to confirm what they were seeing.

The Open Road

Randy shared his experience of reaching the blast crisis with his leukemia and then having it miraculously go back into remission. He told them, "I know my trial with this disease is not over, but I'm so grateful, so very, very grateful that my life has been extended so I can share my message and testimony with you."

He taught them for an hour, often becoming emotional, along with most of the people in the audience. He finished with a challenge that they examine their lives; choose priorities based on God, family, and service; and live their lives in such a way that they would be ready to meet the Lord when he calls them home. He ended his message in the name of Jesus Christ.

As Randy sat down, his mouth drooped and the palsy instantly returned.

Meeting people and shaking hands in the long line that formed afterward, Randy again struggled to speak and had a hard time being understood.

The Bell's Palsy faded away three weeks later and did not return.

Every waking moment, Randy was thankful for feeling good and for being free of pain. He did not slack off in his genealogy work or his speaking; in fact, he picked up the pace. From December to April, Howard estimated that Randy taught, face-to-face, over 5,000 people.

In April, Randy started having the familiar headaches. He felt tired and needed an afternoon nap to keep going. With great reluctance, he scheduled an appointment with his doctors. They confirmed his suspicions. The leukemia was back and in the blast crisis again.

"So how long are you giving me to live this time?" Randy teased his doctor.

"There's no way you are going to get me to venture a guess. In fact, you will probably out-live us all."

Randy thought that statement was pretty funny. Later in the exam, the doctor repeated what he had told Randy six months earlier: "The odds are very slim that you will live beyond the next 30 days." However, this time he added with enthusiasm, "But we have beat the odds before, and I think we ought to go for it again!" They started the regimen of chemotherapy, transfusions, and pain killers that afternoon.

Randy was disappointed by the brevity of this remission but told his dad, "It's in God's hands. I'll do what he wants me to do, as best as I can discern it, then I'll leave the rest up to him."

Based on his previous response to the chemotherapy, Randy realized he could no longer live alone. When Melba's husband Earl was promoted into the hospital administration at Primary Children's Hospital, they had purchased their first home. They invited Randy to live in a spare room in their basement. With this arrangement, he would have only a 20 minute commute to the library, a 15 minute drive to the hospital for his treatments, and Melba could help nurse him on his bad days. He sadly said goodbye to his bachelor apartment and moved in with Melba and Earl and their two young daughters. Randy would never again live on his own or enjoy a day without severe pain.

The doctors continued to be amazed. The 30 days of life they had predicted for Randy—based on all the medical knowledge available to them—turned into 45 days, then 60 days, then 90 days, then 120 days. They were also surprised at how he was holding up. As before, the chemotherapy was causing Randy awful

The Open Road

nausea, headaches, and fatigue. The doctors were concerned, however, because prolonged treatment could actually kill the patient before the leukemia did. His type of treatment and the strong dosages were meant only as a last-ditch effort, but Randy's body was enduring the harsh chemicals, so the doctors continued the treatment. There seemed to be little that was average or normal with this patient. In July, the white blood cell count came close to normal, and though those worrisome blasts were still present in significant numbers, they had been noticeably reduced by the chemotherapy.

A church group of young adults with whom Randy was acquainted decided to take to the "open road." Thirty of them were planning to ride in six motor homes to visit the Mormon church history sites, following the Pioneer Trail in reverse to Nauvoo, Illinois. Then they planned to visit Kirkland, Ohio, the Hill Cumorah Pageant in Palmyra, New York, and on to the temple in Washington, D.C. They invited Randy to come.

Randy's doctors did not like the idea of him traveling so far from their watchful eyes. Randy reasoned the disease was currently manageable, and there were both phones and hospitals all along the way. After a lot of discussion, he finally announced he was going and asked his medical advisors to help him assemble the needed medical support. He filled an old fishing tackle box with pills, medicines, bottles and blood tests, along with instructions and emergency numbers. And on July 15, he headed out on the "open road."

The first motor home broke down 20 minutes after their departure. They lost the next one in Laramie, Wyoming. By the end of the first day, the already crowded motor homes were bursting at the seams. But the excited group managed to organize, compromise, and harmonize. They sang, laughed, told stories, and made do.

And Should We Die . . .

In the early morning hours, rolling over the prairie of Iowa, Randy reflected on the more than 2,000 pioneers who had died trying to escape persecution and reach the valleys of the Wasatch Mountains. He felt humbled as he compared his 30-mile hike in the Uinta Mountains to the pioneers' 1,200 mile trek to Utah. He felt grateful for their sacrifices and thankful for his heritage.

In Nauvoo, Illinois, while others toured the restored buildings of the city abandoned by the Mormons, Randy napped on a bench near the ruins of the temple. His hematocrit count, or the red blood cells which greatly affect one's energy level, had begun to drop.

The motor home caravan drove to the jail site in Carthage, Illinois, where the prophet Joseph Smith was martyred by a mob. Randy felt that God had asked the 38-year-old man to seal his testimony with his blood. Randy wondered if God would ask the same of him.

That evening he developed a temperature of 103 and started sweating profusely. He recognized the symptoms, dug into his medical kit, and took some pills and syrups. By morning he was feeling better, but his hematocrit count continued to drop.

As the adventurers motored through Ohio, Randy's hematocrit dropped lower than it had ever been. He felt drained of every ounce of energy he possessed. His friends rigged up a bed where he could stretch out, displacing several friends who crowded together without complaint. Three returned missionaries placed their hands on Randy's head and gave him a blessing, declaring in the name of Christ that the Lord was mindful of his situation and would protect him, and that he would return home safely to his family. In the evening prayer the group asked God to bless Randy and help him.

Randy borrowed a friend's collection of quotations and while the R.V. motored into the night, he read the words of a philosopher and teacher named Truman G. Madsen: "Fasting is feasting on the Spirit; and somehow not partaking of physical food isn't quite enough. Fasting is a kind of concentration, a kind of pulling ourselves together."

As Randy read those words, he thought about the questions he had concerning his own life. He now desperately wanted to know the answers. As he pondered, he realized that up to this point, he had felt that if he was faithful, things in his life would unfold as the Lord saw fit. Now a new realization was occurring to him. He had not had the faith to receive a direct answer to his questions from the Lord. He now felt different. He felt the Spirit was nudging him, suggesting something different. He felt ideas coming to his mind by way of inspiration. He was being told that the Lord did not want passive "wait and see" faith, though up until now that may have been appropriate. Now the Lord wanted "active faith." He wanted Randy to act on his faith to receive answers to his questions. Randy examined his heart. He was completely confident that he would have every question answered. He glanced at the trip's itinerary. In 24 hours they would be in Palmyra, New York. There would be a pageant of music, song, and drama. Thousands of people would be gathered from all over the world. He would have a chance to walk though the grove of trees where Joseph Smith received his first vision, which led to the restoration of the gospel. And Randy suddenly knew that there, in the grove, he would receive the answers he was seeking. He began a focused fast, concentrating on the questions that mattered most to him, confident that God would answer him.

The caravan stopped at Niagara Falls. Randy left the group and slowly made his way to Goat Island. He gazed at the thundering water all around him. He said a prayer of thanks to his Heavenly

Father for the beauty of this earth, for the pleasure of spectacular scenery, for the strength that comes from beholding God's creations. Randy then asked in prayer that his Heavenly Father please give him direction and reveal His will for Randy's life.

Randy looked at the path that bordered a farmer's wide field; though only a few hundred yards long, the path seemed to stretch on forever. At the path's end was a thick grove of maple, elm, beech, and oak trees. This was the place where his answers would come— if he could just get there. The sun was brutally hot. Randy felt drained of all energy. Each step was a trial, the price he must pay to receive his desire. He felt great anxiety—was he worthy to receive an answer? Did he have the strength to endure? As he walked, he reviewed in his mind the questions he would ask: Am I to be healed of my leukemia? Should I exercise faith toward that end? What about marriage and family? An education? A career? Or am I to go on suffering, being an example to others who suffer? Are there others who need my message? Or, am I to be called home—to die—in order to serve a greater mission? As Randy rehearsed these questions, his confidence grew. He knew the Lord would give him what he yearned for.

Randy entered the grove. The cool shade protected him from the sun. He paused in a clearing to catch his breath. Tourists were milling about, laughing, snapping pictures, talking loudly. He continued deeper into the grove, following a winding trail. The sound of voices faded, then they were gone. He stopped frequently to breathe deeply. Up high, a breeze gently moved the branches, while down below, the forest floor was alive with dancing patches of light. He came to several cut logs arranged into a circle. Randy sat down and rested. He paused a moment longer, then knelt in the circle.

The Open Road

"My Father who art in Heaven . . . " Suddenly, his mind went blank; his carefully considered questions had been removed. Then strong, whispered words came: "The desires of your heart will be fulfilled." He recognized the phrase from his patriarchal blessing—with one slight difference. The word "righteous" had been omitted. Randy thought to himself, "*What are my desires? What are my deepest desires? To receive the Lord's promise that I will dwell with him in his kingdom.*" And something else. As Randy continued to ponder, he thought of the many times he had asked his Heavenly Father for what he desired and then added "nevertheless, not my will, but thine be done." Randy had asked for what he desired but had been willing to submit to God's will. Yet, something now was different. There was no need for him to submit because all he wanted was for God's will to be done. He felt complete trust. If the Lord wanted him to be healed, then he wanted to be healed. If the Lord wanted Randy to die, then Randy honestly, whole-heartedly wanted to die.

Slowly, purposefully, Randy continued his prayer. "My Father who art in Heaven, I desire with all my heart that thy will be done . . . what is thy will?" Randy was immediately engulfed with an indescribable joy filling every fiber of his being. Joy. No pain. No fatigue. Only consuming joy. And while he was immersed in this wondrous joy the words came—sweet, delicious, marvelous words.

A friend helped Randy walk from the grove to the motor home. "You feeling all right?" he asked with concern.

"Wonderful. Absolutely wonderful," was Randy's answer.

After a short ride, two friends helped him out of the motor home and into a folding chair on the grass. Thousands of people were gathering for the Hill Cumorah Pageant. Randy ate a sandwich, though he had little appetite. As the music swelled and the pageant began, Randy fell asleep sitting upright in his seat. A friend noticed and helped Randy back to the motor home. The next two days were a blur. Randy would be awakened to eat, then visit the restroom, then go back to sleep.

In Fairfax, Virginia, the motor home pulled up to a hospital. Randy was becoming less and less responsive. His friends grabbed a wheelchair, and with jokes and the sound of a parade, they wheeled Randy into the emergency room.

Two hours and a battery of tests later, a worried doctor ordered an emergency blood transfusion and immediate radiation therapy. Randy insisted that they call his "personal physician team" in Salt Lake City before he would agree to any treatment. The doctor's all conferred on the phone, then turned on a speaker phone so Randy could join them. Randy was ordered to check into the hospital for a several week stay and strictly follow the Virginia doctors' instructions. The Utah doctors insisted that radiation treatments not be used because he had responded well in the past to the chemotherapy. When he was well enough to travel, he would come to the University of Utah Medical Center to continue the efforts to save his life. The conference call ended with an admonition from one of his Salt Lake doctors.

"Randy, this is the worst situation you have faced since Italy. I want to impress upon you the seriousness of your condition."

Randy smiled, agreed to follow the instructions he had been given, and felt no fear or anxiety.

The "open road" gang gave Randy hugs and kisses and were obviously worried. They all said a prayer for Randy, then gave him $420.00 which they had collected by passing the hat. They explained that it was to pay for his flight home when he was feeling better.

The Open Road

As the motor home pulled away. Randy watched through his tears. He was neither worried nor sad. He was touched by his friends' love and generosity.

It was Beverly's first ride on an airplane. She flew to Washington D.C. to be with Randy and to bring him home. She was anxious about flying, and to take her mind off the flight she struck up a conversation with the middle-aged couple sitting next to her. They asked the purpose of her visit to D.C., and she told them all about her son. When the plane landed, the couple insisted on driving her from Dulles airport to the hospital in Fairfax.

The hospital staff welcomed her, seemed already well acquainted with Randy, and rolled a bed into his room. "You are welcome to stay here as long as you can stand his jokes," they told her.

Randy did not think his mother's trip was necessary—he could take care of himself—but he was overwhelmed by emotion when she showed up. He was grateful to see her. To pass the time during his transfusions and chemo treatments they talked. Randy seemed especially emotional. He asked her forgiveness for being so difficult after Red Castle. He told her how much he loved her and how thankful he was for the sacrifices she and Dad had made raising him. His mother was touched. It seemed to her like he was preparing to say goodbye.

Two days later, the couple Bev had met on the plane called to see how she and Randy were doing. They invited mother and son to go with them to the Washington D.C. temple. With permission from the doctor and a caution to not be gone too long, Randy and his mom accepted the invitation.

The temple visit was comforting, and afterward the kind-hearted couple asked Randy if there was a site in the capital city he desired to see. "The Lincoln Memorial," he said softly.

They parked the car in the small lot south of the memorial and walked to the front. Randy and his mom looked east at the reflecting pool and the Washington Monument. Randy began climbing the steps: one step, then a rest, followed by another step, and another rest. It felt a lot like his final assent of Mt. Wilson a year earlier. Randy stumbled and the gentleman who had brought them sprinted up the stairs and helped Randy to his feet.

"Do you want to go back to the car?" he asked with concern.

"No. To the top please."

Randy leaned heavily on the man and rested at the entrance beside one of the giant columns. As he looked at the statue and read the words engraved on it, Randy began to cry. He said a short prayer of gratitude for the life and sacrifice of Abraham Lincoln, a man who died in the service of his God and country. "Help me to be as selfless" Randy prayed.

Five days after checking into the hospital, Randy was well enough to fly home. "A miraculous recovery" were the words a doctor used. Arriving in Salt Lake City, Randy checked into the University of Utah Medical Center, where the doctors confirmed he was on the mend. Two days later, he snuck out of the hospital to joyfully welcome home the "open road" gang.

Chapter 11

No Fear

"Hello." It was Randy's voice on the phone.

"Yo, Bro," I said as a greeting. "How are you feeling?"

"It's a rough day. Big, bad headache," he admitted.

"Sorry it's so hard."

"Well, it could be worse."

"How?" I wondered, half serious.

"Well, I could have a bad headache and be as ugly as my big brothers!"

"Randy, I hate to break it to you . . ." I teased.

"Then don't," he chuckled.

"Hey, I've got a few questions for the book. Tell me about your trip to Idaho Falls last month."

"It was fun. I got to spend some time with Uncle Mel and Aunt Dixie and the cousins."

"How are they doing?" I asked.

"Fine. They're doing really well. Lance took me and some of the kids up to a cabin near West Yellowstone. We had a great time. He's sure grown up, a senior in high school—hard to believe. He's got more chest hair than you do!"

"Well, you know what they say: hair doesn't grow on stone."

"Who says that?"

"*They* say that. Everyone who knows anything says that," I answered.

Randy continued, "I think the only ones who say that are those who aren't sure of their own manliness."

"Yeah, well, I've got better things to do with my testosterone than grow hair."

Randy laughed. His laugh was contagious. I always loved hearing his laugh.

"How did your talk go?" I wondered.

"It went well. I really feel that I'm connecting with people. I feel the Spirit working through me. Sometimes it's just amazing."

"Write it down in your notes," I admonished.

"I will. I'm spending about five hours a day writing. It's taking a lot longer than I thought it would."

"Now aren't you sorry you didn't keep up your journal after your mission?"

"Yeah, yeah, I know. Well, these notes are better than nothing."

"They *are* better, and what you've written has already helped a lot," I said, hoping to encourage him. "I understand you visited the doctor yesterday, and he said all the signs are looking good."

"Yeah. The blood cell count was down and my hematocrit was up."

"How do you feel about that?" I asked cheerfully.

"Honestly? I'm disappointed," he confessed.

No Fear

By mid-August, with his leukemia once again manageable, Randy began an aggressive speaking schedule. He accepted an invitation from his cousin, Lance, to speak to a church group in Idaho Falls. His talk was well received, and afterward Randy went with Lance, his parents and family, and some of the young adults to a mountain cabin at Island Park, Idaho.

The group built a fire in the fireplace, sat on pillows thrown around the floor, and Lance presented Randy with a guitar.

"Seems like old times," Randy noted, thinking of Ricks College. They sang some sing-a-longs and told stories and laughed. Randy strummed the guitar, playing a slow, mellow tune, then asked the others if they would like to hear a song he had written. Several nodded.

Lance asked, "When did you write it?"

"About two weeks ago. I wrote the words and my brother-in-law, Earl Christison wrote the music." He began singing:

> "Have you ever had that feeling
> as you walk about the earth,
> that something inside is missing
> and you've felt it since your birth?
> I'm so homesick,
> I want to go home.
> I'm so homesick,
> but on earth I must roam.
> I'm so homesick
> until I reside
> at his right side,
> at his right side"

He sang several verses, and when he stopped all in the room were silent. Then an attractive young woman named Sylvia spoke. She thanked Randy for sharing at the fireside and for his song. She explained that she also was suffering from leukemia. She shared with the others her fears and her hopes and her faith. Randy felt a great kindness toward her and appreciated her testimony. The group finally began breaking up as the women arranged their sleeping quarters upstairs and the men sacked out on the lower floor.

Randy was in a thoughtful mood and not sleepy. He sat watching the fire. Lance sat down next to him.

"You turning in?" Lance wondered.

"Not just yet."

Randy studied Lance. In the two and a half years since they had spent the weekend at Ricks, Lance had changed. He had not grown much taller but had added about 30 pounds of solid muscle. He was an amazing football player—a powerful running back—who everyone predicted would have a phenomenal senior year. He had thick, dark hair and though just 17 years old, he had bushy sideburns, something Randy had never been able to grow.

Lance lowered his voice and asked, "Hey, what do you think of Sylvia? Gorgeous isn't she?"

Randy nodded, "She's beautiful on the inside and the outside—a rare combination."

"How about you and Sylvia getting together? You'd make a great couple," Lance urged.

Randy shook his head. "It'll never happen."

Lance looked surprised. "Why not?"

Randy looked at Lance for a long moment as if he was trying to decide what to tell him. Then he said, "Because Lance, she's going to live a long time, and I'm going to die—soon."

Lance looked perplexed. "How do you know?" he asked.

"I had the opportunity to visit some Church history sites a few weeks ago. I visited the sacred grove."

"The sacred grove? In New York?"

"Yes. After fasting, I found a place to be alone, and I asked the Lord His will for my life. I was given a very special experience, very sacred . . . and I don't feel right talking about it. But it was the greatest joy I've ever experienced or thought possible. I learned some important things. Let me just say that I know my time is very short."

"Are you afraid to die?"

"I would love to live and have all the experiences of life. I would love to be married like Melba and have a baby just like her daughter Brook. But my work is nearly done here, and I'm needed for some important work on the other side of the veil. What I want most is to go where our Heavenly Father needs me."

Lance watched the fire for a long while in silence. "What do you feel—knowing you're going to die?"

"Peace. Total, absolute peace."

"No fear?" Lance seemed amazed.

"No fear. You see, Lance, I know God lives. I don't hope or want to believe it. I know it. I know Jesus Christ loves me, you, all of us. He suffered and died for us. I know these things. So dying and going to be with Him is a wonderful thing—nothing to be afraid of."

Lance suddenly brightened, as if he had just solved a mystery. "Have you been promised exaltation?" he asked eagerly.

Randy said gently, "That's not something that should be discussed. Let me just say . . . I know everything is going to be fine, just fine."

Long after Randy's breathing had become soft snoring, Lance gazed at the fire and thought about what Randy had told him. He deeply wanted to know what Randy knew.

And Should We Die . . .

As August slipped into September, Randy resigned from his position at the Ancestral Research Center. He tearfully thanked them for the caring and patience they had shown him.

He met with Ron at the seminary and was energized by their agreement to write a book about his life. Randy reflected on his life and began writing about his experiences. He and Ron met frequently to discuss different events and the people involved so Ron could contact them and get their perspective. And Randy continued to speak.

At a Sunday church service in Tooele, Utah, the bishop introduced Randy in an unusual way. He said, "I'm not going to tell you anything about our speaker today; I'll let him do that. I just want to tell you about how I first heard of him." The bishop explained that a member of their congregation had experienced the death of a loved one. He was deeply hurt and felt bitter toward God. He quit attending church meetings and turned away church members who came to visit him. He eventually asked that his name be taken off the rolls of the church. He spent his days working and his nights alone. One day his oldest daughter and her teenage children kidnapped him. They took him to their home for the weekend. He enjoyed their company and only partly resisted when they dragged him to a fireside to hear a young speaker. The young speaker spoke of terminal illness and death. He spoke of love and hope. He testified of God.

"As the grieving man listened, the spirit of God filled his heart. Instead of pain for the loss of his loved one, his heart was full of gratitude for all they had shared. He felt the love of God and knew that God was mindful of him. He felt a confidence and hope that one day he would be reunited with his loved one. He went to the bishop's office, repented, cried, bore his testimony, and renewed his efforts to be a Christian in every sense of the word." The bishop continued, "He credited that young fireside speaker with melting the barriers in his heart and opening him to the spirit of God." The emotional bishop then finished his introduction with, "I would like to introduce to you that young fireside speaker: Randy McMillan."

Randy had not heard the story behind his invitation. He felt humbled that God was using him to heal others. Randy shared his life with the people in attendance. He spoke from his heart. In addition to his usual message, he added. "I've learned that righteousness is not holding yourself aloof from others or judging their weaknesses and feeling disdain. Lord knows I've wasted a lot of precious time and hurt a lot of people doing that. Righteousness does not come from obeying a lot of rules and then comparing ourselves with others to see who's ahead. Righteousness comes from loving our Father in Heaven with all our heart and loving his children—warts, and weaknesses and all. I've learned that life's greatest joy comes from serving others, loving others, caring for others. That's truly how we serve God. That's how we experience the greatest happiness."

On Monday, Randy was scheduled to speak in Ogden, Utah. He felt awful. He had an excruciating headache and felt dizzy. He called his mom and asked her to speak for him.

On Tuesday, he went in for the usual tests and the doctor announced the results were encouraging. His white blood count was still coming down, his hematocrit count was up.

"All in all the news is very good," the doctor said.

Randy was actually disappointed by the results. He thought he knew what the Lord had in mind, but the medical tests did not support this view.

And Should We Die . . .

On Wednesday, Randy was feeling worse, so Melba asked her mom to come help. Randy was scheduled to speak to a sorority group at the University of Utah. His head hurt worse than it ever had and he was nauseous and dizzy. Melba suggested canceling and he agreed. Then, as an afterthought, he decided to pray about his decision. A few minutes later he told Melba he felt that he needed to go. His mom tried to change his mind and offered to go in his place.

He shook his head. "The Spirit has told me there are two students who need my help desperately. I feel the Lord wants me to go. He'll help me."

They helped him into the car and as they drove to the Sorority House, he started bleeding from his right nasal passage.

"Be prepared," Randy cited the Boy Scout motto as he pulled a gauze roll out of his pocket and jammed it into his nose. A few minutes later, he started bleeding from the left passage. Another roll of gauze came out and ended up in his nose. His mom dug into Melba's diaper bag to get some baby wipes, then cleaned off his face and some spots on his shirt. Randy looked in the rearview mirror at the two rolls sticking out of his nose.

"I guess I'm not going to be impressing any women tonight." Turning to Melba he said, "It's never easy, is it?"

She smiled, "Not if it's worthwhile."

Randy was welcomed and ushered into the sorority house. The young ladies were gracious and led him to a large room, where a group of twenty or so sorority sisters were seated. Randy apologized for the inconvenience, then asked if he could sit because he did not have the strength to stand. They removed the podium and rearranged the chairs into a large circle with Randy at the entrance. He looked at the faces of the beautiful women in the room and felt self-conscious. He was painfully aware of his thin hair, gaunt face, stained shirt, and two blots of cloth sticking out of his nose. He said a silent prayer and remembered the words of Stephen R. Covey from the mission home over two years ago: "Seek to bless, not impress."

"My Father in Heaven, help me to bless their lives I pray," he asked silently. Randy told his audience that he had leukemia and was going to die soon. He talked to the students humbly, sincerely, and with feeling. He told them about his trials and the strengths he had gained from his trials. He expressed his gratitude for adversity and told them he had learned more about our Father in Heaven and his son in the last year than in the previous 21. He testified that we learn about God by experiencing God, not by reading about or listening to others' experiences with him. He shared his belief that adversity and trials had humbled him enough and made the issue of living important enough that he searched for answers to life's questions with real intent. He had offered to God a broken heart and a contrite spirit, and the Lord had accepted his offering and answered his questions. He testified of a God who knows us personally and loves us individually.

The fatigue Randy felt was overwhelming. His headache worsened. He paused a long minute waiting for his second wind to kick in. It did not come. He closed his remarks with a quiet challenge to each of the women to search for this Father in Heaven of which he spoke and to use the adversity in their lives as a spiritual tool and a blessing.

Afterward Randy sat as each sorority sister expressed her thanks and shook his hand. Many were crying. Several initiated hugs. Two hung back and waited until most of the others had gone, then sat in chairs next to Randy. One young lady was sightless due to an accident several years earlier; the other student shyly shared that she had just discovered a few weeks ago that she had a terminal illness and would not survive much longer. Both felt their lives were in crisis, and they were both battling depression and despair. Each had entertained thoughts of ending their lives. Neither was aware of the other's struggle.

Randy held their hands as they wept and expressed their thanks for his message. They asked him questions about the details of his life and what he did to get through each day. He gave them more information about his experience in the grove than he had shared publicly. They thanked him, told him he had helped them "so very much," and both gave him a kiss on the cheek.

Randy needed help to the car, then asked his mom to drive him to the hospital to get his nose cauterized—again.

Chapter 12

The Day of Peace

I took the call in my office.

"Ron, this is Melba. Randy's real bad. Can you please come over?"

I arranged for a substitute teacher and drove the 20 minutes to Melba's house. My sister met me at the door crying.

"I've never seen him this bad. He collapsed on the floor, he's bleeding badly, and he's incoherent—mumbling. I can't understand him."

I walked in the entryway and saw Randy sprawled on the living room floor. Melba had carried a beanbag in from a bedroom and rolled him onto it, cushioning his head and shoulders. Mom was holding a towel against his cheek, under his nose. I knelt down beside him.

"Hey Bro. How ya' feelin'?"

He groaned in return and seemed to be in a great deal of pain.

"I've called Earl and he's on his way," Melba said. "The doctor won't be available until this afternoon, but then he wants to see Randy as soon as possible." Melba was frightened and concerned, but calm and very much in control. The mothering of two young children had trained her to handle emergencies calmly.

And Should We Die . . .

Earl arrived, walked in, and knelt beside me. Melba apprised him of the situation. Diane, Randy's oldest sister changed towels.

"Randy, Randy." I said loudly. He opened his eyes and seemed to see me. "Do you want a blessing?" I asked.

He slowly nodded.

Earl repositioned himself, and we both put our hands on his head.

I called Randy by his full name, and in the name of Jesus Christ, began the blessing. Immediately a feeling of radiating warmth filled me. The words to say were given to me, and I spoke them aloud.

"Randy, your progression in mortality is now complete, and I seal you up to the Lord."

I realized by the words I was saying that Randy's life was now over. I cried as I continued speaking.

"I bless your earthly father who loves you and is concerned for you, with understanding and comfort. And I bless you that you will not suffer unnecessarily, only what is needed for you to complete your trial.

"Randy, before coming to this earth, you counseled with the Savior. He presented you with a choice: to come to this earth and raise a righteous family attendant with all the joys and sorrows of that course, or to come to this earth and take upon yourself leukemia and by so doing, with your example and words, touch the lives of many others who could not be helped in any other way. Randy, you chose this affliction to help others and serve God. And He pronounces: 'Well done thou good and faithful servant. Enter into my rest.'"

Mom, Earl, Diane and Melba began crying, feeling the Spirit and happy for the successful completion of Randy's mission.

The words continued to come.

"Randy, your influence and teaching will still be great; you will continue to teach. Your experiences in this life will give you great power in teaching others who have crossed over and in persuading them of the

166

gospel truths. Your family will be blessed by your passing. In the world of spirits, you will be aware of your family and loved ones and you will, with God's permission, intervene in their behalf. Your prayers and priesthood will have influence and will change their lives for good. Your family will love you and remember you.

"Randy, I bless you that your death will not be untimely, but will take place at the time it should.

"And finally, my brother and friend, I bless you that your mind will be clear so that you can put together your thoughts and feelings to finish your book and express your love to your family.

"I seal these things upon you in the name of Jesus Christ. Amen."

Melba, Earl, Mom, Diane and I continued to weep. I felt immense joy for Randy and privileged to have experienced the Spirit so strongly and been a part of delivering this blessing to my brother.

Randy sat up. He took the towel from mom and daubed his face. Giving each of us a long, serene look and he said, "So it's over, huh?"

I nodded.

He smiled and said, "I'm glad. I'm tired, so very tired."

He motioned to the living room and Earl and I carried him there. Melba placed a pillow and some towels on the couch, where we laid Randy down. The bleeding from his nose slowed, and Mom packed it with rolls of guaze. He asked for a drink of water.

"Have you got your notes?" he asked me.

I had not brought my briefcase. "No. Left the stuff in the office."

He shook his head with mock disgust. "Amateurs. Melba," he called, "I've got this rookie who came to the job without his tools. Can you bring him a pen and some paper?"

Melba brought Randy a glass of ice water and gave me a pen and spiral ringed binder.

Randy spoke quickly as I wrote, providing some details he had not mentioned about the open road trip, along with some thoughts, feelings, and details about the past few weeks. I wrote quickly and after a few minutes caught up.

"Okay," I said, "What else?"

"Why don't you write down my blessing. And," he said dramatically, "my part is done." He brushed his hands against each other back and forth like he was dusting them off. "Now the rest is up to you."

I slowly nodded.

Melba came in and asked if we were finished. After Randy nodded, she suggested we get Randy to the hospital.

Robot-like, just going through the motions, I helped Earl carry Randy to the car.

Melba put the beanbag in the back of her father-in-law's Cadillac, and we helped Randy lay down. I commented that he was going to the hospital in style. I told them that I would call Dad and the rest of the family to catch them up on the latest. There was no doubt everyone would want to come tell Randy goodbye.

Earl's mom came to the house to watch the little ones, and I called my wife. She said she would meet me at the hospital. I placed the calls to the family, then rushed to the hospital where I was directed to Randy's room. His eyes were closed. He was experiencing severe pain behind his eyes and temples. Strong pain killers had not helped. To fight his high fever, Mom was placing cold cloths on his forehead. Melba was massaging his head. As Mom and Earl were talking quietly, Melba noticed Randy motioning to her. She leaned down close to hear Randy's whisper. His words were an effort.

"Do you think they could make me unconscious? It hurts so bad."

"I'll talk to the doctor and see what he can do," she replied. Then she asked, "Randy, how do you feel about dying? Are you afraid? Are you excited? Are you sad?"

"I don't feel anything. I just want to get it over with."

The Day of Peace

A nurse who the whole family had come to know and appreciate came in and began a transfusion of platelets to help slow the bleeding from his nose. She also gave him three units of blood. He slowly started to feel stronger.

The doctor gave Randy a thorough exam and ran some tests. The situation was grave. He explained that Randy's condition was critical and that there was nothing medically to be done. He reminded us that leukemia victims usually do not die of the leukemia but rather are so weakened by the disease they die of an infection or pneumonia. He confirmed Randy was dying, and explained that it could likely be several days or weeks before his life would end.

Over the next few hours, my wife, Dan, Alicia, Amber, and Howard arrived. Each kissed Randy and expressed their love. Randy nodded and was mostly quiet, as words required too much effort. Randy's bishop, William Wright, and his wife arrived to lend their support.

Late in the afternoon a nurse I had not seen in my many visits to the hospital stopped in, looked at the crowd, and said that only three visitors were allowed at a time. No one moved. She left the room a bit frustrated. A few minutes later, the nurse we knew returned and told us not to worry about it.

Randy kept looking at his family—moving from face to face—his eyes lingering on each family member. When he made eye contact, he would wink and nod slightly. We talked about his blessing and his fireside at the sorority. Then people started recalling good times and funny times, and pretty soon we were all laughing. Randy seemed amused and would join in with smiles and nods. Later, a nurse confided in me that the nurse new to the floor could not believe a patient's family would sit around him and laugh at such a somber time, and she said so to a doctor. The doctor had then smiled and told her that he earnestly hoped she would get a chance to know the McMillans.

And Should We Die . . .

At 7:00 p.m., the doctor gave Randy a sleeping pill, and he soon fell asleep. The nurse took his vital signs and announced he was much improved, that he was no longer in critical condition and was resting well. His family began filing out with plans to gather in the morning.

At about 11:00 p.m., Randy's dad patted his hand. His mom cradled his face in her hands and kissed his forehead. She said, "Goodnight my darling. Have a peaceful sleep." They then left for Melba's house. Melba felt she should stay with Randy so a cot was brought in. She moved it next to Randy's bed and laid down. All the lights were turned off except a small night light.

Around midnight, Randy began tossing back and forth in his bed. He groaned and rubbed his head. Melba sought out the doctor and explained that Randy was not sleeping comfortably. The doctor roused Randy and asked some questions.

"Randy. Randy, do you need more medication?"

Randy kept his eyes closed and answered, "I don't know."

"Is what we're giving you helping you?"

"I don't know."

The doctor told Melba to let Randy sleep and come get him if anything changed.

Melba laid on the cot facing Randy. He opened his eyes and looked into hers. He seemed to recognize her, then closed his eyes and went back to sleep. He continued to mumble and groan and say things that did not make sense.

After an hour Melba asked the doctor to examine him again.

"I think he's in a lot of pain," she said.

"Randy," the doctor gently shook him. "Randy wake up. When's your birthday?"

Randy answered, "Two, one, fifty-six."

The doctor looked at Melba and she nodded that the answer was correct.

The Day of Peace

"Do you know where you are?"

"Yeah, you smart aleck," Randy smiled, still keeping his eyes closed.

"Who's the smart aleck?" the doctor rejoined. He then continued, "Seriously, do you know where you are?"

"I'm in the temple, ready to do a session." Randy responded.

The doctor turned to Melba and said, "I think he's only partially conscious. I'll check back in a few minutes."

Melba lay back down on the cot, and Randy reached out and held her hand. Then he asked, "Is this the day of activity, or is this the day of peace?"

Melba answered, "I hope it's the day of peace."

Randy smiled, his breathing slowed, and he slipped into unconsciousness.

At 1:30 a.m., Melba called Mom, then me.

"The doctor says Randy's pupils are dilated and he's completely unconscious. I think you'd better come."

I parked the car at the hospital. The night was moonless. The air was cold. Orion's scabbard scraped the Eastern sky. "Winter's coming," I thought. My wife and I entered Randy's room. His breathing was loud and labored: a prolonged silence would be followed by a great gasp, which would be followed by a loud exhale. Listening to it was painful. He seemed to be suffering horribly. The nurse assured us that his mind was gone.

"He feels no pain. It's just that his body is working so hard to stay alive; he's such a fighter."

Throughout the early morning hours, other members of the family started gathering: Dad and Mom, Blake, Diane, Dennis's wife Peggy, Danny and Alicia and their sons Brandon and Dustin. There were long periods of silence followed by a retelling of a memory of Randy growing up. Occasionally, someone would walk over and stroke Randy's head or kiss his cheek. He continued to struggle for breath. The doctor asked Dad if he wanted Randy on a respirator. After being assured there was no brain function, Dad declined.

By 11:00 a.m., Randy's condition had not changed. Mom and Dad went to Melba's home to shower and change. Most of us went to the cafeteria for lunch. Melba stayed alone with Randy.

Randy's breathing slowed dramatically. He groaned and exhaled for the last time. As Melba looked on, the color seemed to leave his face from the bottom up to his forehead. He was gone.

Melba laid her head on his chest and started crying, then she said aloud, "Randy, please tell me, is it sweet?" She earnestly wanted to know that he was in a better place.

The nurse checked Randy's vitals and went for the doctor. Earl returned, saw Melba, and began crying. "I'm so happy for him," Earl commented as he comforted Melba. As they looked at Randy's still form, Melba felt the sweetness of the Spirit and felt that Randy was happy and pleased with his new home.

When I entered the room, I looked at Melba and Earl, and I immediately knew my brother was dead. I stepped to his bedside, caressed his cheek, and placed my hand on his motionless chest. His tortuous battle for breath was over. I kissed his forehead and softly whispered, "Goodbye, Bro. Well done."

I had been preparing for this moment a long time, but instead of being stoic and strong as I had imagined I would be, I was filled with churning emotions and I wept.

I felt a profound sadness that Randy's last years had been so full of suffering and pain. I felt a deep loss that I would now be without my friend and his reassuring smile. I felt a longing to go with him on the next phase of his journey. But mostly, I felt a sense of sweet relief. I was so glad that my younger brother was finally at rest.

The Day of Peace

That evening, Sept. 28, 1978, the family planned his funeral and began making arrangements for his burial.

Randy's funeral was held on October 3, at the Clearfield Stake Center. The chapel was filled, and over-flow seating was needed to accommodate all those attending. One of Randy's missionary buddies, Kim, sang a song entitled, "Some Dreams Must Wait." Earl and each of Randy's brothers and sisters shared thoughts and testimonies or read one of Randy's poems. Randy's mom comforted family and friends from the podium by expressing her gratitude for Randy's life and her testimony of the Lord's love. A good friend of Randy's named Brian, sang Randy's song, "Homesick."

Many wept as an audio tape played one of Randy's firesides. In the excerpt, Randy read one of his poems, bore his testimony of the Savior's loving kindness, and told his audience not to be sad for him, but to be glad for the joy he had known.

A choir made up of several of Randy's open-road friends sang a popular church hymn that was written and sung as the Mormon pioneers crossed the plains a 131 years earlier:

> "Come, come ye saints,
> no toil nor labor fear,
> but with joy wend your way.
> Though hard to you
> this journey may appear,
> grace shall be as your day.
>
> And should we die
> before our journey's through,

And Should We Die . . .

Happy day! All is well.
We then are free
from toil and sorrow too.
With the just we shall dwell.
But if our lives
are spared again
to see the saints
their rest obtain,
oh, how we'll make
this chorus swell—
*All is well! All is well!"**

On the drive to the cemetery, Randy's cousin, Lance, commented to his family that Randy's funeral was more like a missionary farewell than a funeral, "more of a feeling like 'see you later' than 'goodbye.'"

The family, extended family, and closest friends gathered at the grave site. Uncle Mel offered a prayer to dedicate the grave, while little nieces and nephews played among the headstones of four generations of McMillans. Randy's would make five.

Everyone affectionately shared kisses and hugs, and the throng gradually thinned. On that sunny Autumn day in a mountain valley named Heber, only a few were left to witness the lowering of Randy's body into the grave.

*©The Church of Jesus Christ of Latter-day Saints

Chapter 13

Come with Me

Two months after Randy's funeral, Howard had a severe heart attack. He was rushed to the emergency room at the North Davis Medical Center. His heartbeat had become irregular, then stopped completely. Medical personnel worked feverishly to preserve his life. After several minutes, their efforts started his heart beating again. They continued working on him until they finally stabilized his condition.

Beverly was allowed into the intensive care unit. Though this scene was familiar—Howard's ashen face, the tubes in his mouth and arms, and the monitors and graphs and beeps—it still felt overwhelming. She sat in a chair, patted his arm, and allowed herself to cry.

After several days of passing in and out of consciousness, Howard had not shown much improvement. But one night he awoke and looked at the red digital clock on the wall—2:05 a.m. At that moment he became aware of the most beautiful music. He wasn't so much hearing it as he was immersed in it, being filled with it. Far away, beyond the wall with the clock, someone was walking toward him, surrounded by mist and dressed in luminous white. Fear seized Howard. He was not sure what was happening, but it was unlike anything he had ever experienced.

As the figure approached, Howard recognized his son. Randy was radiant and appeared so happy. Standing in the air, level with his bed, Randy smiled.

"Hey Dad."

"Randy?" Howard whispered.

"Yes, it's me." There was a marvelous serenity and joy emanating from him. He continued, "Dad, you can come with me now, if you want."

Howard was frightened and with urgency replied, "No, no. I don't want to."

Randy smiled. "Okay, okay," was all he said. Then the image receded and was gone. The music faded. Howard was alone in the darkened room with the tubes and the monitors and the graphs and the beeps.

The next day, Beverly visited early. The tubes had been removed from Howard's mouth. She pulled a chair up to his bed. He turned his head toward her and tried unsuccessfully to smile.

The most he could muster was a quiet whisper, "Honey." She leaned closer to hear. "Randy visited me."

Beverly looked puzzled.

Howard continued, speaking rapidly. "He was all white and smiling. He said I could come with him."

Beverly placed her hand on his cheek, then stroked his hair. "Oh Howard, my sweetheart, you miss Randy, and I do too. And you're on a lot of medication right now. I think you just dreamed about Randy."

"No, Mom." Howard was adamant. "I saw him. He talked to me."

Come with Me

She kissed his forehead. "Get some rest now. We'll talk about it later."

Howard closed his eyes. He knew he was not mistaken.

After a week, Howard was still in intensive care. He was awake and in pain and bored. Around noon, Howard heard the music again—wonderful, sweet, and holy. He saw a personage approaching from a distance; it was Randy. Again Howard saw how happy Randy was—his expression was completely joyful. The fear Howard experienced with Randy's first visit was gone. Howard felt only peace and a powerful love.

Randy spoke, "I'd sure like you to come with me, Dad, if you would."

Howard thought Randy was asking him to go for a walk.

Randy seemed to perceive his thoughts. "No, I want you to come with me permanently. I could really use your help." Randy paused, then continued. "Now, Dad, it's not your time yet, so you have your choice." Randy paused again. "Will you come with me?"

Howard thought for a moment, and said, "No."

"Why don't you want to come with me?" Randy gently asked.

"Randy, I have too much yet to do. It would be doing Blake and Mom an injustice. I want to make sure Mom is taken care of and get Blake off on his mission."

Randy smiled. "Okay, I understand. That's fine."

Randy slowly faded away. Howard listened for a moment to the music, then everything went black.

The next thing Howard was aware of was his wife and his youngest son, Blake, standing at his side.

"Hi, Hon," Beverly said. "Are you awake?"

Howard nodded.

Blake and Beverly arranged chairs close to Howard's bed.

"Randy came again. He said it's not my time, but I could go with him if I wanted to."

"What did he look like?" Blake asked.

"He was dressed in white and he glowed. He was so happy. He wasn't as drawn and thin as he was when he died—he looked good."

"What color was his hair?" Blake wanted to know.

"His hair glowed, like a light was shining through it. His hair was white."

"What did you tell him?" Beverly wondered, "when he asked you to go with him?"

"I told him 'No,' that I still had a lot to do here."

Beverly looked into her husband's eyes, then at her son, and as her gaze returned to Howard's, she simply said, "I believe you, and I'm glad you decided to stay."

As Beverly walked to the car with Blake, she said, "Dad has had two chances to go and he's turned them down. You watch, by morning he'll be out of intensive care."

When Beverly visited the next morning, she was informed that her husband had greatly improved and had been moved out of intensive care.

Later that day, family and friends were allowed to visit. Howard appreciated their love and attention. As the last visitors left, he was tired and began drifting off to sleep.

Howard heard a voice and opened his eyes. Randy was standing above the foot of his bed. All around him was white light. Howard did not hear any music, but the familiar sense of peace and love flowed through him.

Come with Me

"I would still like you to come, Dad, if you would. I sure could use your help. Your time is not up, but you can come with me if you want. I'll understand either way."

Howard did not hesitate to reply, "I'm sorry, but I'll have to pass it up."

Randy smiled and said, "I understand." He began to fade, then added, "I love you, Dad," and was gone.

Lying in his hospital bed, Howard felt an overwhelming love for his son. He felt a deep gratitude that his Heavenly Father would grant him this experience with his son—and a quiet hope that in staying, he had made the right choice.

One week later, Howard was released from the hospital.

My father lived another ten years.

Blake served a mission in Delaware and the surrounding area. When he returned, Dad and Mom served as missionaries for a year and a half, officiating in the Washington D.C. Temple. Later, they accepted a call to be missionaries in Louisiana, where they blessed many lives during the eighteen months they served near Baton Rouge. In between, they loved their nineteen grandkids and watched them grow.

Epilogue

The four-hour drive to Idaho Falls parallels the Wasatch Front, with mountain peaks reaching over 11,000 feet. It skirts the Great Salt Lake and presents a reflected view of Antelope Island. The route passes by Clearfield High School and Hill Air Force Base; crosses Bear River, the Idaho border, and the Snake River, and cuts through miles of twisted, black, lava beds. The trip allows time to think.

After Randy's death, I wrote his book four times. Once while living in Salt Lake City, another time in Boulder, Colorado. I rewrote it once in Springville, Utah, and again while living in Modesto, California. I used the manuscript as my thesis toward a master's degree. Writing Randy's story was often illuminating, always painful. But I was never really satisfied with the result. Countless times over the next 22 years, I dug the manuscript out of my files, read through it, and put it away.

I got busy. I went back to school. My wife and I had five children. I changed careers. I traveled a lot. I co-founded four different businesses. Howard, my father, passed away in 1990 after another heart attack. I helped make the arrangements for his funeral. I co-wrote some books and did a lot of church and community service. I struggled though a difficult divorce, remarried, and worked hard at blending two families totaling ten children. I guess you could say life went on.

And Should We Die . . .

But when I'm honest with myself, being busy is not the reason I did not finish Randy's book. I struggled with understanding. How do you write about a topic you do not understand? Why did God allow a young man with so much to offer to be taken? With so much to live for, why did Randy die so young? What was on the other side that could be of greater importance than what Randy was doing here? And some of my questions were more personal. Why did God take Randy away from us? From me? Sometimes, even now, I miss him so much I ache. I miss his smile, his joking, his hugs, his questions, our discussions. I miss my brother.

My attempt to write a story I did not understand amounted to thinking long into the night, recalling some sweet memories and hurting deeply, re-reading some of Randy's journals, interviewing people in his life, then writing and scribbling out and throwing away and fretting and putting the manuscript back in the files for a few more years.

Then I received Lance's unforgettable phone call.

In 1979, the year after Randy died, Lance graduated from High School. He was an All-American fullback and heavily recruited by several major universities. That summer, he injured three discs in his back in a weight-lifting accident, ending his athletic career. He decided to serve a two-year mission for the Church of Jesus Christ of Latter-day Saints. He was called to serve in Finland. While there, he became seriously ill with an undiagnosed malady. He underwent two operations and returned home with the symptoms worsening. After several tests and examinations failed to diagnose the cause of his ailment, he was sent to the Mayo Clinic where they discovered he was suffering from a rare disease called Crohns. The disease causes the intestines to ulcerate and creates a host of painful problems.

Epilogue

Crohns does not usually cause death, "However," the Mayo Clinic doctor stated, "you may very well wish it did cause death, as painful as your case most likely will be." The doctor's predictions turned out to be accurate. Over the next 18 years, Lance suffered through more than 30 major surgeries and over 100 hospitalizations.

In between hospital visits, he married Jozet Miller and had five sons and one daughter. Professionally, Lance became the co-host of the nationally-syndicated radio talk show, "Probing America," as well as the creator and producer of the "What's Right with America" radio segment, which was heard regularly on over 400 radio stations nation wide. By 1998, Lance was serving as president of the American Family Institute, a non-profit organization dedicated to rebuilding America through strengthening the family.

On Christmas Day, 1998, Lance had a motorcycle accident. He was treated at the hospital for a broken hip, and he endured yet another surgery using four long screws to pin his hip together.

What should have been a normal recovery suddenly became abnormal. Lance came down with pneumonia. Extensive infiltrates began collecting in his lungs and blocking the air passages. Lance developed a rare lung disease called Acute Respiratory Distress Syndrome (ARDS), an often fatal illness. His condition worsened. His lungs slowly filled with blood clots, fluid, and infections. He was put on oxygen, yet his lungs could not pass enough through to the blood to keep him alive. On January 10, he experienced respiratory failure and lost consciousness. Lance was rushed into an emergency surgery that lasted five hours. In order to keep him alive, the doctors paralyzed his body and put him in a drug-induced coma. This stopped all non-essential bodily functions; those that were essential were performed through life-support equipment. The doctors told Jozet that Lance had only a 5 percent chance of survival.

And Should We Die . . .

My wife, Bonnie, and I were deeply concerned. Not only was Lance my cousin, he and Bonnie were great friends. In fact, it was Lance who introduced us. We joined family members and friends to fast and pray for Lance's recovery. For four weeks, Lance was comatose.

My wife, children, and I were thrilled and relieved when we got the call from Jozet in February, telling us that Lance had been revived and was rapidly recovering. The doctors told Jozet that it would likely take three months for Lance to learn to speak again, and probably six months to a year to be able to walk again. That's why I was shocked to receive a phone call from Lance in March, saying that he wanted to get together. Lance said he had crossed over death's veil. He said he had met and spoken with Randy and that Randy shared a few things that he really wanted me to know and understand. It was my hope that these things would give me the peace I had been seeking. In April of 1999, my wife Bonnie and I drove to Idaho Falls to meet with Lance and hear his story.

Jozet welcomed us into her home. She was cheerful and gave us warm hugs. I noticed how much her countenance had brightened since we had been with her a few months earlier and the worry about her husband had been weighing heavily on her mind. She led us into Lance's bedroom where they had set up a hospital bed. He was free of tubes and IV's and was sitting partially inclined. Lance greeted us with a tired smile.

"How are you feeling?" I asked as I patted his arm. Bonnie leaned over him and kissed his cheek, her long blond hair hiding his face for a moment.

He smiled broadly and said, "A lot better now."

We all laughed.

Bonnie caught them up on the latest developments in our lives, and then I could not wait any longer.

Epilogue

"Lance, I'm so anxious to hear about your experience. You said on the phone that you had . . . been to the other side? Spoken to Randy?" Hearing myself say it out loud made it sound . . . well, incredible. But I knew Lance, trusted him.

Lance asked for a drink. Jozet took a glass of water from the bed stand and handed it to him. With great effort, Lance held the glass and drank from a straw. Jozet then retrieved the glass.

Bonnie and Jozet sat in chairs close to Lance, and I sat on the foot of his bed.

"After my accident, I got ARDS, a disease of the lungs," Lance began.

"Yes, we remember. We got regular reports from your mom."

"Ron, I died." He looked at me with great sincerety. I was suffocating, unable to breathe. It was a horrible sensation. Then everything went black. I felt myself leave my body and move through the darkness, then I entered into an exquisite light. It filled me with the most profound feeling of love, hope, joy, peace and happiness I could ever imagine. I was surrounded by a world of incredible beauty and splendor. It was so . . . I really don't know how to describe it. It was the most marvelous experience of my life."

I sat transfixed. I had heard of near-death experiences; I had read about them. But to listen to someone I knew and respected—like I did Lance—describe his personal experience with crossing over held me in awe.

Lance closed his eyes as he described what he had seen. His face seemed to convey the sweetness of his memory.

"As I was taking in this amazing scene, I turned to see a group of family members waiting to greet me. In front was your brother Randy. I'll never forget his bright smile. He held his arms open, and we gave each other a long embrace."

Lance opened his eyes and looked at me. "Uncle Howard was there too."

"Dad?"

"Yes," he said, nodding his head.

"What did he look like? What did they look like?"

"They looked wonderful. Randy looked much like he did at Ricks. His face was full, he had all his hair—not at all like when he was dying. Howard looked much younger, thinner, and healthier. They both looked so happy. I saw Grandpa and Grandma Richardson and many other relatives and friends."

"They were so filled with joy and happiness, Ron. It was so incredible to meet with them and to know with certainty that they are still alive, that there really is life after death and that our loved ones are there-in that splendid paradise, that beautiful world of spirits. And Ron, I learned there that they know what is going on in our lives here. Many of them have the opportunity to be a part of our lives.

Lance paused, seemed to catch his breath, then added, "This brings me to the message Randy wanted me to share with you, Ron."

I looked at him anxiously. It had been foremost in my mind in the days since Lance's call. What was it that Randy had shared with Lance and wanted me to know?

Lance asked for another sip of water. He had trouble holding the cup and Jozet helped him drink. He took a deep breath and continued.

"Ron, Randy wants you to know that it is okay—that it was and is right."

"What is right?"

"His death. He calls it 'his passing'. He said you have questioned his death for all these years and that you have been upset with God for having taken Randy when he did.

Epilogue

I sat in silence. This was hard for me to admit to myself; it was something I had never mentioned to Lance.

"Randy knows a lot about your life because he has been very involved in your life. One of his assignments from God has been to watch over you and your family and be of service to you. Ron, Randy didn't conclude his service to God upon his death, he had only begun that service. You see, many of the good, righteous people who die are used by God as ministering servants, angels if you will. They continue to learn and grow, use their talents and be of service to Heavenly Father's children—including their own families.

I was honestly feeling a bit overwhelmed. This was absolutely amazing. A message from my dead brother! Answers to questions I had been wrestling with for so long. But was Lance telling me the truth? Did he really see and talk with Randy? Had he somehow imagined all this?

Lance continued, "Randy explained to me that often God answers our prayers by sending unseen servants to assist us. Often, those servants who are sent are our deceased family members who love us so much. And so, Randy has continued to be part of your life. And he serves the Lord in many other ways, as well. Ron, the very things Randy had been promised he would do with his life are things he is accomplishing right now. His life has continued beyond his death. As Randy stated it, 'Death is not the ending; it is but a transition'. His work and service has not ended, but only changed to a different realm. There were significant reasons for that. He is currently fulfilling the things he was always meant to do with his life, and has just passed to the next stage of his life."

Lance stopped and looked into my eyes. He seemed to be gauging my reaction.

I had no reason to doubt his sincerity. I closed my eyes and felt a warm familiar feeling—a strong sense of light and comfort, a wonderful peace.

"I believe what you're saying Lance, I believe you. And I have so many questions!"

"Randy said that you would have a lot of questions. He said the answers would come to you if you sincerely seek them. Take time to read the scriptures, pray, ask your questions, write down your impressions. Randy promised that if you did this, you would be given many answers and much more understanding. He also said that when you pray and become filled with God's Spirit that on occasion you will be able to feel Randy near you and feel his concern for you and his love for you."

Lance's words were exciting. Randy's message to me was comforting. I felt hopeful. I eagerly anticipated feeling Randy's love and friendship again, and yet, I did not feel confident about my ability to discern the Spirit and understand.

"I'm not so sure I can do that Lance. I mean I have felt the Spirit before, I have received impressions, but I'm just not sure..." My voice trailed off as I wondered if I would be able to act on Randy's invitation.

"Ron, I don't know what to say. The way I've experienced it is if you prepare yourself, ask our Heavenly Father sincerely, you will feel the burning light of truth within you. Only the Holy Spirit can create that feeling. You've felt it before."

"I know I have, but, on occasion not regularly or consistently. "

"The scriptures say 'ask, seek, knock' and they promise you shall receive. I think, confidence comes over time. We have to learn to trust those thoughts which are associated with that good, enlightening feeling of the Spirit. As we act on these promptings and as we see the good, in some cases even miraculous things, that comes from doing such, we are able to gain greater faith in the process. We come to know that the thoughts and feelings coming into our hearts and minds are indeed from God, sometimes being conveyed to us by his unseen servants, our loved ones."

"Ron, one last thing. Randy said there are many who could be helped by reading about his experiences and testimony. Finishing his book and making it available will help him fulfill his mission."

Lance was clearly showing signs of exhaustion. I fought the urge to ask more questions. I felt a sense of illumination. A quickening. I'm not sure how to describe it other than I felt the Spirit was confirming the truth of Lance's words.

We thanked Lance and Jozet and promised to get back together when Lance's strength had improved.

On the long drive home, Bonnie and I silently pondered Lance's heartfelt message. I determined to immediately arrange my schedule for an escape to the mountains to ponder, pray and learn.

There is a hidden place—little known, seldom visited. I went there in search of answers and understanding.

I parked my car at Sundance on the east slope of Mount Timpanogos, then hiked a ridge which parallels a splashing stream below. After winding through the oak brush and aspens, I took a rest in view of Stewart Falls, where the stream cascades down several hundred feet of cliff. But instead of hiking down to the icy waters, I veered right and traversed a steep, wooded slope along a hard-to-find trail known by only a few.

And Should We Die . . .

The path leveled out above the cliffs just long enough for me to catch my breath. Then I began a strenuous ascent through lush green stone terraces laced with snow-melt springs. I followed the trail until it faded out on rocks, crossed the stream at the base of a thin, misty waterfall, and scrabbled up the talus slope to the saddle—a rounded pass between two craggy peaks.

At 10,000 feet above sea level, the sky was a clear, amazingly bright blue. To the east, the snow-capped Uinta Mountains filled the horizon. I knew that below their highest peak, out of sight, Red Castle lay hidden. Closer, I could see the soft green of the Heber Valley, and closer still the dark blue waters of Deer Creek Reservoir.

I continued over the saddle and entered Provo Hole. Invisible from the mountain's base, Provo Hole is several hundred acres of jagged rock and broken snowfields surrounded on three sides by sheer cliffs, some nearly a thousand feet high. It was the perfect place to camp and to think . . . and to pray.

I set up a simple camp, sat on my sleeping bag, and leaned against a rounded boulder. I read some of my favorite scriptures and was quiet.

In the tops of the Wasatch Mountains on a moonless night and under an awe-inspiring sky, I expressed my thoughts and feelings to my Father in Heaven. In the name of his Son, I asked my questions, I asked for direction, I asked for help. And as I prayed in that mountain stillness, I felt Randy beside me. I did not see him as my father had, nor did I touch him in any physical sense. Yet I knew he was with me.

My time alone in that mountain refuge was one of the sweetest experiences of my life. I felt my brother's love for me again in a most personal and profound way. I was taught by the Spirit. I came to the realization that the most important part of my prayers had been missing, the listening part. Now, listening in the stillness is to me the most crucial aspect of praying. I know that our Heavenly Father

will teach us through His Spirit and through His ministering servants, at times, as well.

That night I wrote down the impressions that came to my mind
and heart that were associated with the feeling of the Spirit. I believe
that our departed family members-those with good, loving hearts-are
used by our Heavenly Father to carry feelings and messages to our
hearts and minds. It is often when I receive such impressions that I
feel closest to my brother and father. It is in those moments that I
feel they are beside me whispering encouraging thoughts and adding
their faith and prayers to mine. I believe that, in looking back, I now
recognize some times when Randy was present in my life, helping
me, sent by God to assist me. I believe I know why Randy died when
he did. It was always meant to be so. It was part of Randy's life plan,
the plan he helped develop and agreed to before he was born. No
one's death is untimely or unnoticed, of this I am now most certain.
God knows the end from the beginning and he brings his children
home at the appointed time for sacred, loving reasons.

"Death is not the ending; it is but a transition," Randy told
Lance. It has finally come to feel that way to me. I don't think of
Randy or Dad as dead anymore. I know they are still nearby, serv-
ing, loving, and watching over me and my family.

I have not visited the Spirit World as Lance has, but my witness
of these things, received from the Spirit, is just as sure.

I think Randy might conclude this book, if he were writing it,
with a statement something like this:

"Life's greatest joy comes from loving and serving,
regardless of your circumstance or situation. When
things are worst for you, look to serve others and you
will experience relief, hope and love. Do not mourn our
passing, for we are yet here. We are filled with the

unspeakable love of God in a realm of consummate beauty. It is wonderful here, we are so very happy. And the pain, struggle or suffering we experienced on earth was but a small price to pay for the knowledge and joy we have gained here. We did not conclude our work in death, rather we have been given the opportunity to serve in ways that we could not in mortality. We have come here to complete our callings, our commitments to God, and our work for you. We love you and are often near. Seek to feel our love for you by immersing yourselves in the Spirit of God. That is when you will feel us closest. We shall see one another again soon enough. Now be at peace, knowing there is in reality a hereafter."

I recently drove through the towering rock walls of Provo Canyon, wound past Deer Creek Reservoir, and entered into a green valley protected by the majestic Mount Timpanogos. I stopped at a cemetery on a hill and sat on the grass between the graves of my father and my younger brother. I laid a copy of this manuscript against Randy's granite headstone. This book was begun 23 years ago as two brothers talked of things that matter. I helped write it as a favor and also to continue Randy's work, hoping with trepidation that these written words might benefit and touch a few hearts in the same way that his spoken words had during his life.

As I knelt and thanked God for Randy's life, I realized something I had never before supposed. The person most blessed by the book Randy had asked me to help him write so many years ago was me—his older and forever grateful brother.

fin. 2-3-10
Excellent

Author's Notes

Medicine has made extraordinary strides since Randy's passing. Leukemia is no longer the death sentence that it used to be and treatment is no longer such torture. If leukemia is a part of your life, ask your doctor for information sources that will help you realize the options available and the many reasons there are for hope.

Howard's visitation from Randy after Randy's death, while unusual is not unique. In fact, there are many examples of this type of experience throughout Mormon History. For example, consider a reference in the 2002 Priesthood manual:

> The President [David O. McKay] then took occasion to relate an experience in the life of Bishop John Wells, formerly a member of the Presiding Bishipric. A son of Bishop Wells was killed in Emigration Canyon on a railroad track . . . . His boy was run over by a freight train. Sister Wells was inconsolable. She mourned during the three days prior to the funeral, received no comfort at the funeral, and was in a rather serious state of mind. One day soon after the funeral services, while she was lying on her bed relaxed, still mourning, she claims that her son appeared to her and said, "Mother, do not mourn. Do not cry. I am all right." He told her that she did not understand how the accident happened. He explained that he had given a signal to the engineer to move on and then made the usual effort to catch the railings on the freight train, but as he attempted to do so his foot caught in a root and he failed to catch the hand rail and his

body fell under the train. It was clearly an accident. He said that as soon as he realized that he was in another environment he tried to see his father but he could not reach him. His father was so busy with the duties in the office that he could not respond to his call; therefore, he had come to his mother and he said to her, "You tell Father that all is well with me. I want you to not mourn anymore."

When I had the experience mentioned in the epilogue, I was not familiar with doctrine that deceased family members can become ministering servants to living family members. Since then, I have learned that several Mormom leaders have taught the same. Joseph F. Smith wrote:

> NATURE OF MINISTERING ANGELS. We are told by the Prophet Joseph Smith, that "there are no angels who minister to this earth but those who do belong or have belonged to it." Hence, when messengers are sent to minister to the inhabitants of this earth, they are not strangers, but from the ranks of our kindred, friends, and fellow-beings and fellow-servants . . .
>
> In like manner our fathers and mothers, brothers, sisters and friends who have passed away from this earth, having been faithful, and worthy to enjoy these rights and privileges, may have a mission given them to visit their relatives and friends upon the earth again, bringing from the divine Presence messages of love, of warning, or reproof and instruction, to those whom they had learned to love in the flesh. (*Doctines of Salvation*, pages 435-436)

William is not the actual name of Randy's friend described in Chapter 8.

About the Authors

Ronald Glen McMillan is a nationally renowned speaker, author, and consultant. He received a B.S. degree in sociology from the University of Utah and a Masters degree of Organizational Behavior at Brigham Young University.

Ron co-founded both the Covey Leadership Center and VitalSmarts, LLC, and has consulted with business leaders from Disney, Nike, Ford, Saturn, Harley-Davidson, Lockheed Martin, Ford, and many others.

Ron is the author of numerous articles and co-authored the New York Times best seller *Crucial Conversations: Tools for Talking when Stakes Are High* and *The Balancing Act: Mastering the Competing Demands of Leadership*. After five years of research into a variety of articles and ancient texts, Ron co-authored two historical novels, *Zion: Seeking the City of Enoch* and *Zion: The Long Road to Sanctification*.

Ron is on the Board of Directors for the American Family Institute, a non-profit organization dedicated to rebuilding America by strengthening the home. He and his wife, Bonnie, are the parents of 10 children and currently reside in Utah.

Randy Lee McMillan graduated from Clearfield High School as a popular student leader, athlete, and musician. He attended Ricks College where he was a member of the "Freedom Singers."

Randy has a passion for genealogy and served as Vice President of the Ancestral Research Center in Salt Lake City.

Randy has received much acclaim as a speaker throughout the intermountain west, addressing issues of Terminal Illness, Dealing With Adversity, and Finding Hope Through Service.

And Should We Die . . .

Randy is one of seven brothers and sisters and sees his purpose and hobby as serving others. He currently resides in an undisclosed location.

Available Now

Fireside
with Ron McMillan
on CD or Cassette

Pick it up at your local bookstore or order at our website
www.americanfamilypublications.com

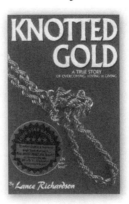

"He appeared out of Heaven, nearly 2.000 years ago, and prophesied of our day . . ."

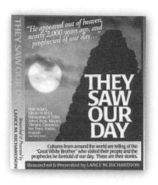

They Saw Our Day

Researched and presented by Lance M. Richardson

Cultures from around the world are telling of the "Great White Brother" who visited their people and the prophecies he foretold of our day. These are their stories.

*Hopi Indians*Kikuyu of Africa*
*Mahayanas of China*Aztecs*Mayans*Tibetans*
*Cherokees*Nez Perce*Pueblo*Iroquios*

Fascinating stories from cultures around the world detailing the prophecies they have received concerning our day.

Only $14.95 for two cassettes
Order at www.americanfamilypublications.com
or call 877-622-5205

"This book will bless the lives of those ready and willing to seek the healing touch of the Lord."

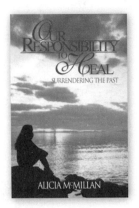

Our Responsibility to Heal
by Alicia McMillan

For thirty years she lived with the pain and anguish due to the child abuse she suffered at the hands of her own father.

Countless years of concealing her past and keeping this 'family secret' destroyed her birth family. Now it was threatening to destroy all that she had hoped to build with her own family. Peace and comfort seemed to elude her in her search for freedom from her troubled past. The haunting memories of her youth and the pain and depression of her adult life almost claimed the most important part of her; her spirit.

In "Our Responsibility to Heal," Alicia McMillan describes her personal journey on the path to healing as she shares the sacred and miraculous blessing of being touched by the healing hand of the Lord."

Out in paperback. Only $12.95 each.

Pick it up at your local bookstore or order at our website
www.americanfamilypublications.com
or call 877-622-5205